Thomas Ellis

Non-Human Thought

Non-Human Thought

The Mysteries of the Animal Psyche

JACQUES GRAVEN

Translated from the French by
HAROLD J. SALEMSON

Stein and Day / *Publishers* / New York

Contents

Non-Human Thought

Preface

The Appearance of a New Science

SOME prefaces are mere chores to write.

First, because readers hesitate to venture into them, but also because one sometimes agrees to write a preface for a book out of friendship for the author or publisher, but without real interest in the work.

As to the first circumstance, I can, of course, only wish that it may not occur. As for the second, I feel quite confident. The subject Jacques Graven deals with is full of interest. Although a specialist in the subject matter, I have not become jaded, and I always read with pleasure any new writings about the animal psyche.

Nevertheless, on reading this book, certain remarks come to mind, certain facts which require prior discussion. Therefore, going beyond the framework of a conventional preface, we will try to say a few words about animal psychology, its evolution, and its tendencies.

However, the reader in a hurry, the one who does not read prefaces or, at best, reads only the first few lines of them, may with assurance omit this preface and go ahead with the book; I hold it to be a serious work, containing only that degree of error inherent in any human creation. For other readers, I will now go into a very long digression.

Any science, and my own most singularly, goes through crises, and fads. Everyone is always someone else's reactionary or revolutionary, and principles burned at the stake yesterday will be honored tomorrow. This fact in itself is not bad, but, since the revolution reaches the general public only with delay, since the public even sometimes may miss part of the cycle, a certain amount of quite understandable confusion may result.

⟨ THE PRIDE OF "REASON"

So let us go very far back, to the seventeenth century to be precise. Not that questions about animals were not asked before that, but simply because one must choose some starting point. The master thinker of the period, on this subject, was unquestionably Descartes, who, in five pages of his work, *Discourse on Method,* influenced the thought of several generations. *Instinct and reason, the signs of two natures:* this formula was to remain, in France at least, for a long time in the realm of untouchable dogmas. I would not be surprised if some professors still assign it as a subject for philosophical dissertation.

All of Descartes' contemporaries and the following generation, of course, did not necessarily share this opinion—far from it. But its authoritative character, applicable here as elsewhere, during many long years forbade any deeper discussion of it. Nevertheless, if philosophical circles were willing during all of the eighteenth century to accept ready-made formulas, other men were pursuing very pertinent studies. Réaumur, François Huber, and those who emulated them, attempted an analysis of instinctive behavior which modern researchers would not need to be ashamed of.

⟨ SEARCH FOR A METHOD

The principal contribution of these authors is of a methodological character: they observe before speaking out. Their research was as detailed as possible, and it is especially in this sense that they can be called modern. Moreover, it must be recognized that the discovery of what seemed most unusual at the time, the psychic activity of insects, was to lead Réaumur to describe it with an enthusiasm which was at times deplored.

In order to discredit observation, a method which he practiced very little and accused of a certain blindness, Buffon wrote then with sarcasm: "One is filled with admiration that the more one observes the less one reasons." Today, we no longer agree with this desk-bound scientist, whose work no longer lives except as excerpts studied as examples, doubtful at best, of an excellence of style, or in some libraries, because of the splendor of their bindings. Réaumur, despite his excesses of enthusiasm, will remain the one who was able to mark off a few landmarks in the forward march of a science and thereby facilitate the work of his successors. No scientist could aspire to more.

ᵧ TRUTH IN NATURE

A few researchers, therefore, in that century, were establishing the bases of the rational study of insect psychic action. The psychology of higher animals was to take longer to emerge from the shadows. A new school might have been born, however, under the guidance of Georges Leroy. This contributor to the great Encylopedia brought out, from 1762 to 1781, a series of *Philosophical Letters on the Intelligence and Perfectibility of Animals,* which are of the greatest interest and which, especially, are not academic suppositions but the result of observations made in the heart of nature. It should be pointed out that Leroy was a lieutenant of the hunt of the forests of Versailles and Marly and therefore had great opportunity for putting into practice what he advocated in one of his letters: "The naturalist, after having carefully observed both the internal and external parts of the animals and ascertained their use, must abandon his scalpel, leave his study, go into the woods to follow the movements of these sentient beings to judge the developments and effects of their faculty of feeling, and see how, by the repeated action of sensation and the exercise of memory, their instinct rises to the level of intelligence."

The clan of observers therefore took over from that of the reasoners. During the nineteenth century, animals were to be studied with great care. Unfortunately, the observers often displayed insufficient discipline, and their interpretations totally disregarded the non-human character of the animal. Only Lamarck reacted against and combatted this assimilation of the animal to man, known as anthropomorphism. But the positive aspect of Lamarck's contribution in this area was very slight, and his views had scarcely any influence.

As far as those we have accused of anthropormorphism are concerned, we must admit that they were both very numerous and highly variable in their gifts. Alongside the great Darwin and the estimable Lubbock, we find Romanes, who still cuts a fairly good figure, and alas! how many others whose names it is more charitable not to mention. Darwin's work is unquestionably full of insights of genius into animal psychology. His book on the expression of emotions contains the germs of a number of ideas which many take to be of much more recent origin. His writings on the adaptation of insects to flowers, in which he endorses the theses of Sprengel, are full of prophetic views the depth of which is only today beginning to be appreciated. But often, it must also be recognized, Darwin goes too far, and some of his naïve conclusions make us smile today. Thus, he tells us the story of two snails set down in a particularly arid garden. The stronger of the two, he tells us, abandoned "his companion to his weakness" and went over the wall to seek his sustenance elsewhere. After being away for 24 hours, he came back to find the abandoned one, and together they set off to the Promised Land he discovered during his expedition. "The snail seems capable of affection up to a certain point," Darwin affirms.

Then suddenly, in a few years, the state of mind changed completely. Animal psychology now claimed to be a science. Just as the chemist was discovering that a whole could be decomposed into its elements, the psychologist, disregarding complex phenomena, turned his eyes toward the most minuscule details and threw himself into the study of the reactions of animals to supposedly simple stimuli. Research on the variations of speed of reaction in various circumstances became quite the thing to do.

It must be pointed out that research in human psychology was, at the time, exactly at the same point. In that field, however, experimenters sometimes knew how to dramatize the interest of such arid work. For instance, Exner, in 1874, published a work showing the effect of alcohol on the speed of reaction; he deplored (in the *Archiv. für Ges. Psychologie*) that the consumption of two bottles of Rhine wine changed his own score from 0.1904 second to 0.2269. This detail is mentioned here not only to amuse us, but because it shows that the "new wave" were no less naïve than the anthropomorphists, who were to be drowned in ridicule by the whole scientific world from that time on.

⁊ JACQUES LOEB AND TROPISMS

In 1888, a dramatic new development: Jacques Loeb discovered tropisms and announced that certain actions of animals were merely the result of physical forces, light or weight. A whole new school of animal psychology was then born in Germany which rapidly came to the point of denying the existence of its own subject of study.

Although differing radically from Loeb in his "world view," von Uexküll reached similar conclusions. He asserted that a struggle to the death was about to take place between animal psychology and comparative psychology, which could result only in the disappearance of the former. This does not keep us from recognizing a debt of gratitude to von Uexküll, to whom we owe the concept of *Umwelt,* the universe as known to each species as a result of its sensory perceptions and the meaning it attributes to objects.

The German school was not to be satisfied with merely denying the existence of the science whose progress was its goal. It tried to make it totally hermetic by creating out of whole cloth an intolerable jargon. Hearing became "phonoreception." Instinct was renamed "cleronomic associations," apprenticeship "embiontic associations," with consciousness becoming "antiklisis." "Tango-reflex"—no doubt coined by divination, for the dance of that name did not yet exist—had something to do with the sense of touch. This vocabulary, which was very extensive, rarely crops up today.

In America, a new word was being made fashionable by a number of writers who were no longer interested in anything but the "behavior" of animals. The British spell it "behaviour," the French call it "comportement," and the Germans "Verhaltung," but the meaning of the term (actions of animals) comes from American authors. Among these, the best known is certainly Jennings, who studied a large number of animals, though essentially very inferior ones: protozoa, sea anemones, worms, etc. Loeb, for his part, studied mostly insects.

So the two authors, with very different sets of preconceived ideas, concentrating on very different animals, went galloping off on completely divergent paths. Jennings, the apostle of comparative psychology, purely and simply denied the existence of tropisms. Loeb, who invented tropisms, denied that comparative psychology existed as a science. Under such conditions, dialogue became absolutely impossible, the more so as their students tried to outdo the masters.

Jennings's discoveries were not negligible; they added up to the theory known as "trial and error." Any action by an animal is the result of apprenticeship; it heads toward a source of stimulus only because progressive trials have allowed the elimination of errors. To Loeb, on the contrary, it was always a matter of an obligatory and mechanical response.

No doubt both of them were both right and wrong at the same time. Their devotion to their systems served as a set of blinders, absolutely forbidding them to go forward in any way except along a narrow path to which they tried to reduce the entire universe.

What was going on in France during this time? It is scarcely possible to speak of a French school; there was no over-all movement guided by a single idea. A few isolated names, and those of some small groups, can however be mentioned.

⸙ THE LIVING ANIMAL

First, of course, we must pay tribute to the great Fabre. Through his careful observations, he built up a body of work which a naturalist always rereads with profit. He, too, knew the value of studying animals in their natural habitat, and a few lines of his *Entomological Memoirs* form an unusual echo of the letters of Georges Leroy: "You disembowel the beast, whereas I study it alive. You turn it into an object of horror and pity, while I give it love; you work in an atmosphere of torture and dissection, but I observe under a blue sky, to the accompaniment of grasshoppers; you try your reactors on the cell and the protoplasm, I study instinct in its highest manifestations; you scrutinize death, I scrutinize life." Nevertheless, we must recognize that he did not have at his disposal the theoretical foundation necessary to interpret his remarkable discoveries correctly. And particularly, though for different reasons, while he had many imitators, he had no disciples.

Giard, Bohn, and others then launched a new idea, that of the ethological method. At first, this idea was most appealing. It was very "modern," and we are sometimes amazed on reading these authors to see how close they were to modern animal psychology. In this new conception, *ethology* was "the study of the relations of living beings to each other and with the various circumstances of the external world. Nature, with its varied conditions, is one vast field for experiment." What was new in this was that the study was no longer merely of the individual in his surroundings, but of the surroundings themselves and the relations between the individual and his surroundings.

However, Giard's work was much more physiological than psychological, and Bohn had no followers. His collaboration with Piéron quickly dissolved into open conflict, of the most extreme violence. The two researchers delighted the readers of the *Proceedings of the Society of Biology* by "murdering" each other from one issue to the next. This quarrel between two talented men was probably what kept French animal psychology and particularly the ethological school from becoming an active force. This is no doubt too bad.

Elsewhere, a Russian genius, Ivan Petrovich Pavlov, discovered the conditioned reflex. With the 1904 Nobel Prize, his influence became enormous—so excessively enormous that for a long time the Russians would admit the existence of no other school of psychic thought, and to them this one chapter represented the whole book.

Quite rapidly after that the situation became chaotic. Disciples remained as unbending as their masters, or more so, without always having their gifts. For example, while the gobbledygook dreamed up by von Uexküll did not keep him from clearing up for a long time certain aspects of animal behavior, Nuel, a professor at Liège, wrote, "No, there is no such thing as comparative psychology. Let us get rid of the illusion!" And he waxed indignant at the poor reception given the new vocabulary, without compensating for these exaggerations by any positive contribution.

These struggles went on for a long time; they are not all finished yet, and, here and there, some retardate from time to time still picks up the torch of the earlier schools. We may disregard these carryovers. There are sometimes some interesting minds among them, who even do some worthwhile work, but they have the grave fault of no longer being in the stream of things, nor are their works those of genius. There are two ways of being up to date: one is to keep in the swim, the other is to outdistance everyone else.

Events, however, proved the correctness of those who hold that the spirit blows wherever it will. While the specialists defied each other from the dignity of their professorial chairs, other people, all unaware, held the solutions. Two such, Whitman and Heinroth, totally ignored the great streams of thought of the specialists, or at least did not bother to try to connect their own ideas with the fashionable discussions. They were satisfied to observe birds, the one pigeons, the other ducks. The birds were raised for their own pleasure.

These two men, professional zoologists both, loved animals passionately, and the study of animal behavior was only a hobby to them. Sometimes, they published their observations or conclusions, but only in confidential publications, unavailable or very-highly-specialized. Yet, as early as 1898 for Whitman and 1910 for Heinroth, without knowing each other, they both made the fundamental discoveries which paved the way for progress in the knowledge of the animal psyche.

↗ FINALLY LORENZ

Konrad Lorenz was also a zoologist and friend of animals when he enrolled in the courses of a well-known teacher of animal psychology, Professor McDougall. The young student was to note with amazement that his master, pontificating from the height of his professorship, had never looked at an animal attentively. In a laboratory modeled after that of the physiologists, wearing a white smock, as if afraid of being stained with blood or corrosive products, he asked questions of the white rat, was concerned with its response but very little with the animal itself. What he cared about, really, was how many mistakes the animal had made before completing so many trips through a maze. To watch the rat while it was on its way seemed to hold no interest for him, and as for watching it live in between exercises, that was an idea that did not even occur to him.

Yet, animals, even rats, live, eat, copulate, react to their mates, their children, their rivals. They dig shelters, select a home, store up reserves of food, in short, act in very complex ways, and life is a maze which is more complicated by far than the ingenious devices of the psychologists. Struck by the contrast between the sterile methods of laboratory psychology and the revelations he had gotten from his own observations, Konrad Lorenz, when he returned to his home in Austria, went right to work.

He then not only created a new animal psychology by assembling all the most interesting ideas of his time and throwing his own, very original indeed, into a melting pot with them, but beyond that he created a school of work. He was able to surround himself with friends and associates among whom we find very famous names: Tinbergen, Baerends, Köhler, Hediger, etc. The school took on the name of *objectivist,* without, however, having much in common with the objectivism of the German mechanicists of the beginning of the century.

It called the object of its study ethology, quite unaware of Giard, who had doubtless anticipated part of the truth. The postwar period was to see this school definitely recognized. I well remember its first international congress held in Westphalia, with only a few participants, most of them German.

Two years later, a congress held at Oxford brought together 62 researchers, and then in 1959 America discovered objectivism. A very strong delegation from across the Atlantic at the congress at Cambridge indicated the breadth of influence of the Lorenz school. Since then, the position of the objectivists has grown consistently firmer, and the number of professorships of animal psychology, or more properly animal ethology, increases each year in the universities.

In the book we are about to read, we will find presented the basic discoveries of the objectivists, with the exception of certain theoretical developments which it would be difficult to include in a work intended for general readership. I would therefore not wish to predigest the work I am prefacing and will not go into the discoveries of Lorenz and his school.

Would it be possible to restrict modern animal psychology to the objectivist school? However great the latter be, it would be unfair to hold this view. It is only possible to say that there is nothing worth consideration which is diametrically opposed to it.

But the famous von Frisch, the genius who discovered the language of the bees, does not specifically belong to this school, and his entire body of work is outside this stream of thought.

The French school of ethology is another case in point. The first labors of Grassé on termites were in line with objectivism, but for a variety of reasons, particularly World War II, no contact was ever established with the objectivist school. Yet, without knowing each other, Grassé for termites and Seitz for fish each separately discovered the same law concerning the possibility of a group of stimuli adding to or replacing each other.

Though less expressly formalist than the German, a French school of ethology was born. It differs essentially from the other through its field of interest. Germans and Anglo-Saxons have concentrated mostly on vertebrates, the French have studied mostly insects. The French school even selected a more restricted scope for itself, having concentrated on the study of the highly diverse and attractive world of social insects, Grassé and his students working mostly on termites and ants, while Chauvin brought together a team entirely devoted to the study of bees.

In this area, France makes a fairly good showing, but for the rest they are unfortunately somewhat the poor relations—not that they do not have excellent researchers, but that they are very isolated. Very often working in laboratories which are not mainly concerned with these questions, they are hampered because they do not have the optimum fields of observation. Often, too, they are objects of suspicion, for their methods and their work schedules seem extraordinary.

This, of course, brings us to ask other questions. What will the future be in this sphere? The business of being a prophet is even more difficult than that of being a historian, and I will not try to make sweeping predictions. Only one thing is certain: the objectivist school will be left behind. One can only wonder whether it will make the forward step itself, or whether it will be left behind by some new group.

ʳ BEYOND OBJECTIVISM

Certain signs of senility have unquestionably appeared already, and curiously mostly among the younger members of the group. A tendency to repeat the work of Lorenz or Tinbergen mechanically is apparent. Some keep going around in circles, studying insignificant details endlessly, or else, on the contrary, they launch into outrageous generalizations and systematizations.

However, as long as Lorenz and a few others are running the school, any danger of sclerosis seems unlikely. Did not the grand master of objectivism suggest, a few years ago, that the use of introspection be introduced into the study of the animal psyche? Before we pounce, let us listen to him: we all get a certain pleasure from holding a pretty, healthy, lovable infant in our arms. By introspection, we know that the pleasure we feel is of a kind different from certain others—from sexual pleasure, for instance, whatever some psychoanalysts may say. After having felt this pleasure, a normal man would be hard put to leave such a baby in a dangerous situation, and he certainly would not in any case want to do it any harm.

We can note the same behavior in an animal with regard to young animals. The adult animal most ferociously set on defending its territory will be all sweetness to a lost baby, even if it is a stranger. From this it is possible to hypothesize that the same frame of mind, the same mood exist in both animal and man.

This step is easily taken when we observe how human babies, those of mammals, and those of birds share a striking set of common characteristics. Could this set of physical characteristics not be called "touching," without too much anthropomorphism?

Naturally, this is a dangerous step to take. If we do it too fast, we run the risk, unconsciously, of falling into the same old errors. But if we do not take it, if we are too timid, may we not be losing a chance to enrich ourselves? "If you close your door to all errors, truth will remain outside," as Rabindranath Tagore has said.

It is this door which Jacques Graven has deliberately opened. He has brought into his book some facts which are as controversial as they are disquieting, such as animal calculators or those who seek out their masters in unknown places hundreds of miles away.

As far as the animal calculators are concerned, the official explanation seems quite satisfactory. It will be found in the book. But those who support it are rarely honest enough to quote the facts and experiments which appear to contradict it.

As for the second example, that is quite another matter. The press regularly reports quite unbelievable stories. As I write these lines, I have a recent newspaper before me. In it is reported in detail the adventure of a pet hawk which followed its master who had gone from Sète to work near Lyons, some 225 miles away. The bird knew nothing of its master's destination. So this is an incontrovertible case of "psi-trailing." Incontrovertible, at least, to the extent that the authenticity of the fact could have been or was carefully verified.

This kind of verification, which perhaps no one actually made in the case just mentioned, has been carried out by some American authors. They worked with care and an irreproachably rigorous method, and their conclusions, as you will see, were definitely positive. What must one think of this? One is free to choose, to believe that one day these facts will take their place on the canvas of our knowledge, or that, on the other hand, our present-day data are so fragmentary and incomplete that such facts and others will totally upset our ideas about the animal psyche.

At any rate, whatever it may be permissible to think, it is difficult to deny. The latter course entails the risk of appearing ridiculous. As witness that distinguished Sorbonne professor, François Picard, who, in the preface to one of his otherwise excellent books, wrote the following in 1933: "The Armand Colin Collection is not a library of wonders: at the risk of displeasing the lovers of the fantastic, we will not take into account the dreams of a von Frisch or the conversations danced out by the bees . . ."

⌇ THERE IS NO HARMFUL RESEARCH

Those dreams are today being taught in that same Sorbonne from which they were once denounced, but the lesson has still not been learned.

Nevertheless, between total, unconditional credulity and absolute faithfulness to the dogma of received ideas, there is a comfortable margin. In this area, it will always be advisable to act suspicious not toward facts or ideas, but toward methods.

There are no harmful subjects, but there are harmful methods. These harmful methods are to be found in areas where they bother no one because their respectability is never questioned. Yet, there as elsewhere, they do their harm.

We have covered some very rough paths in a science that is still young. On these paths, the researchers often pull in opposite directions. Yet, in spite of their sometimes contradictory positions, most have contributed to its progress, but only to the extent to which they know how to obey the essential principles of the scientific method.

Let us allow the scholar to draw false conclusions, but let us be very demanding about the manner in which his premises were reached. Jacques Graven's book gives us an ample harvest of such premises. May each reader draw fortunate conclusions from them!

JACQUES LECOMTE
Chief Researcher
French National Institute
of Agronomical Research

Foreword

✦

The Animal Psyche,
a Question without an Answer

✦

JUST where will the science of tomorrow come from?

Facts unknown today will become commonplace within the next century. Are we capable of discerning them in the strange laboratory investigations which so-called serious people accept only grudgingly, as if humoring a fad which will eventually disappear?

We have merely to look about us to see that most of the active doers, whether they be airplane pilots or explorers underground, use or apply techniques which often were not yet in existence when they came into the world.

It is not unreasonable to think that in studying the work of the animal psyche specialists, we are watching the birth of new techniques of tomorrow.

At any rate, their work tells an extraordinary story about that strange universe we come in contact with each day in which animals live as if in a world parallel to our own.

It is not without some ambition that we set ourselves to explore this most difficult area, for there are, within the realm of the animal psyche, a certain number of problems which classical studies quite simply disregard. Much animal behavior thus evades any analysis and often even any classification. It is hard to say whether or not it is superior to ours; it is essentially alien to us. And one must use the latter term in its true sense when considering the animal psyche.

Indeed, neither the motivations nor the sensations of animals can really be communicated to us, and, by this very fact, the significance of the world around us is totally unimaginable without prior study.

This is what accounts for the development of a method of investigation often used in animal psychology, that which aims at finding significant stimuli. It is useful to examine this method which opens a window on the unknown. Such a method might be the only one if tomorrow we were to find ourselves concerned with some extraterrestrial psyche.

At the foundation of any such study is the ethogram, the meticulous recording of those actions constituting an animal's behavior. The naturalist makes extensive use of his eyes and his pencil for observing, noting, and sketching, but he is also capable of mobilizing the whole arsenal of modern technique. Binoculars, infrared equipment for night vision, tape recorders, movie and still cameras, telescopic lenses, all have become essential parts of the scientist's equipment.

With these, the researcher analyzes with precision the slightest actions of any animal or group of animals, creating what are known as behavior catalogues, in which everything will be noted, without any omission whatsoever, for the tiniest detail may turn out to be important.

In this way, we learn what is usual and what is not, and we can describe with assurance each movement of the animal. Never again, as was sometimes done in the past, will mating dances be mistaken for combat, to cite only one example.

With the use of decoys, the observer turns into an experimenter. Having observed the animal's response in a specific situation, he tries to isolate what were at first called significant stimuli, which are now known as triggers. He will try to bring about, through an artificial reproduction of the stimulus, a response identical to the one he observed in normal circumstances in relation to the natural object. When this response has been obtained, the experimenter gradually modifies the artificial object used as a stimulus until the response disappears. In this way, it is possible to discover with certainty the parts of the object to which the animal reacted. (Obviously, certain factors outside the object must be taken into consideration also, factors inherent in the animal or in the surroundings.)

If I study the roasted chestnut's attractive stimulus to the human species, the results will be influenced by the satiety of the eater's stomach as well as by, say, the temperature of his environment. I will therefore have to eliminate the errors caused by these variables.

I will then double-check, by confronting the animal from time to time with an object we know should provoke a certain response, which can then serve as a basis and point of reference.

Finally, and above all, we will have to retain an open mind. Nothing should appear shocking to us, unless it be experimental error, and the most outlandish hypotheses should not unduly surprise us, for it is a very strange world, indeed, into which our investigations are at times going to take us.

✓

Animals among Themselves

✓

TO believe that animals live in isolation is a mistake, for even those of the species known to be solitary come out of their solitude on numerous occasions: the study of their family and sex lives offers a wealth of discoveries which becomes an embarrassment of riches when we try to draw up a short table of this specific aspect of their existences. We are obliged to omit numerous facts lest the list become endless. Since a choice is necessary, why should we not limit ourselves to those animals which we can see practically every day?

Let us take for example the hen and her chicks, a commonplace sight often studied by naturalists.

Barely out of the egg, the chick feels the need to cuddle against a warm body, but it would be wrong to think it seeks exclusively the contact of its mother's body. In fact, it feels no need for feathers, but only for warmth, and the caress of a human hand will be enough to calm its peeps of distress, as would be the warmth of an infrared lamp. Yet if the chick is raised by its mother, other "tranquilizers" come into play. The mother hen's cackling becomes operative on the chick about ten minutes after hatching and is enough to quiet its apprehensions.

Not content with having recorded this observation, specialists in gallinacean psychology—they do exist—have gone further into the study of the mechanics of this tranquilizing effect. Tape recordings have allowed analysis of the essential characteristics of this cackling and even its improvement. Thus, if we increase its volume, it tranquilizes the chicks much more quickly and for a longer period. This is a process for which one can readily see the application: if, in the huge hatcheries where hundreds of chicks are kept, this consoling sound is broadcast from time to time in outsize amplification, the reassured chicks will fatten more rapidly. It is an idea which may be considered for some future concentration camp: would it not be possible to find in the human subconscious the elements of a comparable "conditioning"?

The effect of this cackling also suggests other questions. Does the chick instinctively know the significance of his mother's voice or does he have to learn to recognize it? To find the answer, the ears of several chicks were plugged up, making them deaf; and the plugs were later withdrawn so as to compare their reactions, at that time, with the behavior of other chicks. During the first eight days of deafness, there is scarcely any difference between the two groups. As soon as they are able to hear their mothers, the chicks who have never heard any sound at all react just like the others. But if the experiment is extended beyond eight days, the chick no longer shows any reaction and, psychically, will remain forever deaf to the maternal call.[1]

What does this strange experiment teach us? In fact, its interpretation is delicate. Of course, the recognition of the cackling and its sedative effect is innate for the chick, but if experience does not reinforce the instinctive knowledge within a certain period, the instinct disappears and its disappearance is irreversible.

Another question: can the chicks of one brood tell their mother from another hen? To answer this question, two broods of chicks belonging to the same strain are spread about in a dark room, along with their mothers; after a given time, a light is turned on, and it is found that each brood—whose members have been previously

---

[1] A very curious case of parents making themselves known through an innate mechanism was established by Peters. He tried to find out how young fish of the genus *haplochromis* sought refuge in their mother's mouth. He confronted the newly-hatched young with a wax decoy, of the same size and shape as the mother. This decoy had an opening at the exact place of the mouth of the fish which had been used as a model.

When the decoy remained stationary, the little fish seemed to pay no attention to it. But it should be noted that it is only when the mother starts to move that the progeny seek refuge in their original shelter. When the decoy was animated, the result was the same. The decoy became even more effective when two eyes were placed, as they should be, above the mouth, but if the eyes were placed below the mouth, the little fish seemed deeply upset.

ringed with identifying bands—has grouped around its own mother.

Let us try the experiment over again in a lighted room, timing how long it takes the chicks to form a family group. We will find that the assembly takes place much more rapidly if the mothers are of different colors.

So here is one fact to be noted: the color of the fowl plays an important part, and if we put two broods, respectively hatched by a white hen and a black hen, into a room in which there are two strange hens of each of these colors, we will see the chicks scramble without distinction to either of the white hens or either of the black hens. However, they are not so easily duped, and if among a group of other hens present there is their own mother, artificially dyed or disguised, they know how to recognize her immediately. In all of these cases, "mother" means the hen which the chick first saw on his hatching and which continued to take care of him. Confronted with the mother who actually imparted life to him, the chick will display no emotion whatsoever.

Among wild fowl, young birds in the nest, assisted by very special morphological structures, recognize very well the parents who feed them, and, instead of reacting with an attitude of fear or attack, they open their beaks wide to greet them.

For instance, the heron has a white plume on the top of his head. When he comes close to the nest, he bows in such a way that the little ones see this plume, which serves in effect as his "clearance." One day, Lorenz, studying these birds, did not hide well enough and was noticed by the heron just as it was about to make its bow. Upset by the presence of an observer so close by, the heron forgot to identify himself and was forthwith attacked by his brood, which had failed to recognize him as their father.

Among the signs which help baby animals to recognize their mother, one must note the white spot which is to be found under the tail of certain animals, as for example the roedeer. This characteristic sometimes leads to strange mistakes. For instance, the Germanic countries require their cyclists to paint the rear fenders of their bicycles white. This white spot has sometimes misled fawns separated from their mothers, and bicycle riders have found themselves followed for great distances by a fawn without being able to understand the sudden attachment.

The degree of "knowledge" of an animal at its birth is certainly a function of its prenatal development. Some have time to learn, others not. Among birds, we can distinguish those which have a long childhood from the ones which can very quickly do without their mothers. Among mammals, the differences are also very marked. The rat, for example, after a short gestation period—21 days—is born naked and blind, whereas the guinea pig, after a gestation period three times as long, comes into the world with wide-open eyes and covered with fur. The baby hare is in the same state as the guinea pig, whereas the newborn rabbit is as helpless as the baby rat.

ı   A D O P T I O N   O F   T H E   M O T H E R   B Y   T H E   C H I L D

Many animals have no or only a very incomplete innate knowledge of their parents. A gosling adopts as its "mother" the first moving object it sees after hatching. A duckling adopts the first moving object, provided it is no larger than a stooping man and quacks in a characteristic manner. The water hen will accept only an object of the approximate size of its mother, but the shape of the object is of no importance, and a crackerbox pulled at the end of a string can perfectly well create the illusion. The baby chick, as we have seen, pays particular attention to the cackling.

This phenomenon, known as impregnation since Lorenz's studies on the subject, is very widespread among birds and a fascinating subject to look into. What could be more curious than a gosling adopting a human or at least allowing a human to adopt it?

One of the most striking characteristics of impregnation is its complete irreversibility. A young goose, separated from the human whom it adopted in the first seconds of its life, even if placed under the wing of a mother goose among other goslings, will literally die of starvation and distress.

To know what the mother represents for its progeny is, however, only one aspect of the question. There is still the problem of what the progeny mean to the mother.

Here again the barnyard chicken, through its behavior, can teach us a great deal. Thus, during all the experiments which we have just mentioned, the mother hen, far from remaining idle, actively went about keeping her brood together and reassuring the worried chicks.

In this case, the frightened chick's call for help plays a vital role. A few simple experiments can easily convince us of this. If we tie a chick up out of sight of its mother, it quickly starts to peep at the top of its lungs. Immediately, the hen stops eating or scratching the ground; visibly upset, she looks all about and keeps seeking her child until she finds it.

Now let us place the chick under a hermetic glass bell. Although it can see its mother through the glass, it nevertheless calls for help and cannot be heard. All of its behavior shows its panic, but the mother pays no attention whatsoever. In her eyes, that little white ball of feathers bouncing around in silence has no connection at all with her chick.

To find the explanation for this strange limitation, we have to go back to the evolution of the domesticated chicken. The jungle hen, ancestor to our barnyard variety, no doubt had numerous occasions for losing sight of her progeny without thereby ceasing to hear their peeps, whereas the opposite could never have occurred. A strange economic law comes into play here: the hen believes only what she hears and anything else has no meaning to her.

ʏ THE ARTIFICIAL CHILD

The seagulls and mews which abound in our ports have been studied by many naturalists. In particular, two of the founders of modern animal psychology, ethology, specialized in the study of gulls: Baerends and Tinbergen, both Dutchmen.

The hatching gull keeps her eggs warm in a simple depression in the sand. She will sweep any foreign objects out of this depression and will carry into it anything she takes to be an egg. This rather peculiar behavior considerably facilitates the job of an experimenter who wants to know what idea these birds have of the egg.

The imaginations of researchers found an ideal outlet in this problem. They exposed the gulls to a whole assortment of artificial eggs: round, square, and rectangular; some were given strange colors; others were heated or refrigerated. And all of these experiments revealed a strange paradox: for the gull, the ideal egg, the one she seems to consider a true egg, is not at all like her natural egg. Gulls, like some other birds, prefer, above anything else, eggs which are eight times the size of their normal eggs, and it is a strange spectacle indeed to see the setting gull perched over this monster, which rolls around under her body. She is obviously delighted with what is happening, to the point of neglecting her brood for this grotesque decoy.

Several hypotheses have been adduced to clear up the mystery of this weird behavior. Some call it a "vice," while others point out that human beings also have a penchant for hyperbole: the cult of the oversized American car is proof enough. Besides, it is not out of place to underline that exaggeration of the significant stimuli is a constant law of nature.

Biologists have given the name of hypertely to anatomical structures of outsize dimensions such as the exaggerated growth of the crest or egret of certain birds or of their tail feathers and the antlers of deer or elks which, in addition to being gigantic adornments, may also serve as weapons or tools.

This tendency to exaggeration is to be found not only in the higher animals, but in invertebrates as well; the pincers of the stag beetle or of the uca crab attest to that.

⌁ RELATIONS BETWEEN MALE AND FEMALE

From the relations between animals and their young, it seems natural to go on to the study of sexual relations. Reproduction is of course a major concern of the animal world for, in order to survive, a species must have a rather high reproduction rate.

One of the most striking aspects of animal sexuality is sexual dimorphism. The two sexes very often display morphological differences so great that in some cases they have led us to assume the existence of two different species where in fact there was but one.

This differentiation can take on the most varied aspects. As far as size is concerned, we note that the male is generally larger than the female among mammals, whereas among batrachians (amphibians without tails) the opposite seems to be the invariable rule. For birds and insects, there is no general rule. The queen bee is about the same size as her mate, but in termites the queen is distinguished from him by her impressive corpulence.

Among herbivores, distinction between the sexes is marked mostly by the presence or absence of horns or antlers. Horns are common to both sexes, though more highly developed in the male; antlers, generally speaking, belong exclusively to the male.

Archaic mammals had a distinguishing feature in the development of the canine teeth. Only the boar family and related animals have retained this mark of virility.

The matter of coloring is no less strange. Among birds, as an almost general rule, the males eclipse their modest females through the great splendor of their plumage. Even when the colors are almost identical in male and female, as is the case of the finch or the thrush, those of the female are generally duller.

The male butterfly also displays sumptuous colors in many cases, and numerous batrachians, when the mating season arrives, burst out in brilliant colorings. Nor is it unusual for fish to change their colors during the season for love.

Among mammals, however, these variations are less frequent. It is usually by other attributes that the male distinguishes himself: the antlers of the deer family, the mane of the lion, and so on. All of these differentiated characteristics have their use, of course, since in certain cases they allow the animals to recognize easily the sex of others of their own kind.

One of the most interesting experiments in this area is the one tried by Cinat Tomson at the end of the first quarter of this century.

Parakeets have very few sexual differences. The male is recognized only by one minor detail, the color of a spot located at the base of its beak. This spot, blue in the male, is brown in the female. A male, while gladly agreeing to share his cage with a female, on the other hand attacks any intruder of his own sex ferociously. In view of this peculiarity, it was decided to try to deceive a male parakeet by putting into its cage another male whose spot had been artificially dyed and a female transformed in the same manner into a male.

Sensitive only to this significant detail, the male was easily fooled and attacked the false male while at same time courting the equally phony female.

Still, just as a disguise did not completely fool the chicks when it came to recognizing their own mother, conjugal love does open the eyes of parakeets. If one of the partners in a couple of some duration is taken away and disguised by a stroke of the brush, the mate is not misled and his conduct in no way changes.

₁ FROM CHARM TO ARTIFICE

There is a curious parallel between the sense potential of a species and its sexual pageantry. Most mollusks have very under-developed sight, and the sex pageantry, it is supposed, must be of a tactile nature. It is also probable that the chemical senses, taste and smell, play a part.

Among cephalopod mollusks such as the cuttlefish, for example, sight is highly developed, and visual nuptial bait is consequently tendered by the male to the female. The male cuttlefish assumes a very unusual coloring at courting time; it is a black and purple striping on the whitish background of the skin. During the courting process, the male displaces himself, all tentacles outstretched, in such a way as to show off his design to the best advantage.

Outside of the obvious and immediately effective triggers, animals have certain more subtle means of recognition which have still defied our analysis. Here again, as in the case of the egg, it is possible to create models whose sexual attraction is stronger than that exercised by the real object.

Tinbergen and a team of Dutch naturalists studied the attractive effects of the female agrestic or rustic butterfly. The female of this butterfly has a brownish tint; by giving her a sharply darker hue she is made much more attractive to the male, and she can become absolutely irresistible if given a size clearly larger than normal.

The manner of flying also plays its part: the model must be made to move in a zigzag as butterflies do, for no other type of movement proved more effective, nor even as effective.

Morphological structures aside, the various behavior elements act as triggers in a way which seems much more difficult to "improve on" than that of coloring or the general shape of the animal.

Perhaps we should not be too surprised at this, when we see to what degree of perfection these courtship maneuvers attain. Dances, pageantry, demonstrations of the most varied types are common among birds as well as among insects and mollusks.

But the preliminaries to mating are not always long and com-

The dance of birds, the dance of men: isn't there more than one similarity?

Crowned cranes.—Photo Dragesco

The beautiful nuptial dances have often made us believe in the existence of esthetic feeling among birds.

Penguins.—Photos Camera-Press

plicated. At times, the frequency of the act allows no room for any ceremony: the record for sexual potency is held by a rodent, the *meriones shawi,* which can copulate as many as 224 times in two hours.

ı SEDUCTION

Since we cannot list the seductive wiles used by all animals, we will mention simply a few which are particularly curious or original.

For instance, there is the gardener bird, which we will come back to in Chapter X. These birds live deep in the forests of Australia and New Guinea. In order to attract females, they go through a very strange ceremony. Before indulging in the ballet figures which lure the females, the gardener birds first build their theater. This is made up of a framework of branches and twigs decorated with moss, flowers, and mushrooms, and enclosing a cleared-away area: the stage.

On this stage, the bird sets out his props, differing according to the species, but especially remarkable for the spotted gardener. Any object which is out of the ordinary attracts him, and he has nothing against quantity. He is a veritable collector. In the case of one gardener, there were no less than 1,300 sheep's vertebrae carefully laid out.

The habit of spreading out colored objects in his garden sometimes makes the gardener bird most useful. In regions where opals are found, prospectors often think it more profitable to work over the collections made by the birds than to go searching the river bottoms.

The gardener will show the same zeal in picking up any new object—bits of glass or porcelain, discarded cartridges—and will even go so far as to venture into houses to carry away spoons, forks, coins, and so on. An armaments factory located in the forest had to put wire netting on the windows, for screws, bolts, and other small pieces disappeared at an alarming rate.

Once this collection has achieved a certain size, the bird begins his show: he dances around the stage, picks an object up in his beak, catches the rays of the sun on it, puts it back in place, and takes another. All to such good effect that the female can no longer resist. She comes down from her branch, watches first as a spectator, and then joins in the dance.

The nuptial dances of certain animals are so striking that men have very often imitated their choreography and introduced it either into war or religious dances or into their own erotic ceremonies. There is, for instance, the dance of the cranes done by Theseus on his return from Crete along with the young men he had freed. The Jivaro Indians do a dance which imitates the movements of the rock hen. The Siberian Chukchees duplicate the nuptial dances of the ruff, which because of the postures it assumes is known as the battling knight, the Monumbos of New Guinea that of the cassowary, and we could go on to an endless list of such bird-inspired dances.

Europe has not been exempt from such influences since in Bavaria there is a dance which very faithfully copies the movements of the woodcock.

ʏ O R I G I N S   O F   T H E   W E D D I N G   P R E S E N T

Another interesting ceremonial is that of the food offering. This is a very common occurrence among the empididae, a group of gnats which, despite their microscopic size, have been very scrupulously observed by various specialists.

Among certain species of these gnats, the male brings the female a small insect. Sometimes this prey is devoured by the female alone, sometimes by both mates before or during copulation. With other species, the prey is not eaten, but the sight of it acts as an indispensable stimulant. Still other species have a more refined ceremonial: the prey is tendered to the female in an attractive wrapping, a balloon of silk or of saliva. With others, finally, the balloon does not contain any edible prey, but only a fragment of a flower petal, or even nothing at all. In these cases, the female can be seen going through the motions of mastication before acceding to the advances of the male. The balloon is dropped to the ground, and it is not unusual to see a particularly sly male take it back and offer it again to a second female who will then become a bargain-rate conquest for him.

A grasshopper, the *oecanthus,* has on its back a gland which secretes a sweet liquid which the female may drink during mating. A male spider of the *pisaura* genus gives his female an insect to eat during the act. It is true that he may not be doing this without ulterior motive, for there are numerous female spiders who devour their mates immediately after or even during copulation. So his gesture may not necessarily be one of gallantry. Such a procedure has not been discovered by the male praying mantis who, very often, is also devoured under such circumstances.

Among birds, the custom of the offering also seems quite widespread. According to a British ornithologist, Armstrong, we should perhaps see this action as the ancestor of the kiss. At any rate, there are numerous birds which, during pre-mating ceremonies, do kiss or at least rub their beaks against each other. Some herons regurgitate food into the beaks of their females during coupling. One American bird, the road runner, often brings a lizard as an offering

Certain birds are models of conjugal fidelity.

A cormorant asking for a kiss.
—Photo Dragesco

The twig that changes into a monster: the strange world of insects deserves, more than any other, the epithet inhuman.

A battle between praying mantises.—Photo John Gajda

after the sex act. Many seagulls act similarly. Sterns or terns, graceful seabirds, also make use of the food offering. But its essentially symbolic character becomes evident when we note that the female, after having insistently begged for food from the male who is making advances to her, seems to lose interest in the fish once it is given and as often as not gives it back. Let us not draw any comparisons with what happens in the human species under similar conditions. At any rate, such comparisons come to mind too readily to require that we do more than suggest them.

Outside of their family or sex life,[2] many animals live very independently.

We will leave aside, for future consideration, those animals which have an organized social life, and we will now see how an animal reacts toward one of his own kind who is neither his mate nor his child.

✔ CONVENTIONS

Very often, the animal divides the space he occupies into two zones. One of these is his vital domain: that is the maximum surface which the animal has explored. The other, much smaller, constitutes his territory. This zone, which is strictly residential, has the characteristic of being off limits to any other animal of the same species, except for the owner's mate or progeny.

The dimension of the territory varies considerably according to the species but is usually much more restricted than is currently believed if one imagines that wild animals, devoted to freedom, wander ceaselessly through the wide world from one region to another.

The territory of carnivores is naturally rather extensive since more space is needed for hunting than for grazing. A lion needs a territory of some 7,500 acres, while a troop of howler monkeys

---

[2] The sex behavior of the Scandinavian salmon was particularly well studied in Sweden by Fabricius. At first, the female, when she has just selected a spot in which to make her nest, is quite unapproachable. She attacks any individual of either sex who tries to come near her. When the nest is completed, she allows the approach of one male who, after fertilization, joins her in guarding the territory surrounding the nest.

can get along with 250 acres. A buzzard hunts on about 650 acres, while a swan remains within some 300 to 375. A heron observed in the Galapagos Islands lived within an area of 500 square yards, and the little anoli lizards, so common in the West Indian islands, usually stay within some 45 square yards.

The limits of these territories are familiar to the animal who, very often, will go to the trouble of marking them off so as to discourage intruders.

Certain insects have their territories, too. The field cricket, for instance, is very good at defending the approaches to his lair. It is around this aggressive defensiveness that Chinese adepts have for centuries been organizing cricket fighting tournaments. It is also on the defense of their territory that Siamese bettors place their wagers when backing fighting fish.

⸙ THE FRONTIERS

Often the different cries and noises made by animals are intended to notify other beasts of their presence. Their territory is, in fact, the ground over which their voices can carry, in a system which recalls the unit of measurement used until only a few years ago in some of the poorer regions of France. Land was sold by the "earshot," that being the surface comprised within the limits of audibility of a human call.

There are also olfactory markings. All those who own male cats know something about this, and people who walk their dogs and allow them to sprinkle lampposts are only complying with the antiquated observance of a very ancient law.

Numerous other mammals, the hippopotamus among others, mark the outlines of their territory with their excrement, but very often these animals also have special glands for this purpose.

The male cervicaprine or reedbuck antelope marks off his territory by depositing at the tips of tree branches the secretion of a gland located under his eye, and the castoreum set out by beavers at certain spots of their territory probably accomplishes the same end.

Sometimes this marking takes on a particularly deliberate and active aspect. The brown bear brutally scratches the trees which are at the outer limits of his hunting ground and along the trails he must use. The European bison uses his horns to tear off the bark of trees, urinates on the ground, rolls in the mud thus formed, and then with his shoulders rubs the mud into the scars left on the trees.

For fish, on the other hand, there is no possible way of marking, and no way of sound signaling. This leaves but one resource: a small territory and a vigilant watch along its frontiers.

The stickleback, a small brook fish, is a magnificent example of this type of proprietor. After having selected a territory in which it will build its nest to which it will attract its female, it sets up a rigid guard along the borders. Any male stickleback that appears to be planning to encroach is ferociously attacked, and usually the intruder does not persevere.

THE ANIMAL AT HOME

Within the animal's home territory, there are zones of quite different values. First of all, there are the privileged places which are the animal's shelter in case of danger or merely his resting place. Usually, one of these shelters becomes the "fortress," being considered the safest refuge by the individual, the couple, or the social group occupying the territory. Other auxiliary shelters may be used in other circumstances.

Springs, salt deposits, food reserves are also important places, and all of these locations are connected by a series of passages making up a very definite network. It is curious to note that after the death of the occupant of a territory its new owner often retains and maintains the pathways created by his predecessor. And, in many regions of the globe, the passages used by big game are taken over by man, who little by little turns them into usable paths; it has even been claimed that some of the French national highways, with their sometimes unaccountable twists and turns, still follow the traces left by the aurochs in the heart of the forests of Gaul.

It was the Swiss zoopsychologist Hediger who pointed out that animals are enclosed not only in a well-determined spatial frame, but also within an equally rigid time schedule. A very large number of observers agree in recognizing that punctuality is one of the true animal qualities. One of them observed a bat which, during an entire week, passed before a given spot at exactly 9:05 PM, another a blue fox which each day arrived near his cabin at precisely 4:00 PM. Finally, Shiras kept tabs for a period of seven years on a porcupine which, every evening, appeared at the same hour at the edge of a lake.

To conclude this discussion of the animal's territory, we will now see how the animal sets himself up and organizes life on his land.

ᵍ AN OBJECTIVE STUDY OF AN INVASION

Let us once again take as our example a very common animal: the gray mouse.

A few years after the last war, an English naturalist wondered how mice went about invading a house and how they then organized the territory. Beyond his scientific curiosity, he had other reasons to ask himself these questions: the damages caused by mice in goods warehouses, and the means of combatting them, were his special concern.

It was thanks to this concern that he was able to carry out his research on a scale which is rare when the work has no practical application. Dr. Crowcroft obtained the use of an abandoned RAF hangar, and within it he built a veritable apartment of several rooms. These different rooms had portholes which allowed him to observe without being seen. Here and there wooden cases were set out, and, on the floor, Crowcroft had sawdust spread about so that the comings and goings of the animals would leave visible traces.

Then some mice were put in one of the rooms, and the occupation and organization of the territory was observed.

The first days, the animals were extremely cautious and scarcely moved away from the walls while exploring their domain. With time, they grew bolder; they dared to move away from the walls, cut corners, and finally make a rapid dash across the room.

After exploration, exploitation of the territory began. One of the crates became the fortress. From this central strongpoint, divergent trails went out, dotted along the way with auxiliary shelters and temporary refuges. The pathways as well as the limits of the territory were marked off with urine, and, after two or three days, the mice had acquired a perfect knowledge of the topography of the place. At the slightest alarm, they scooted, always by the straightest line, to the nearest secondary shelter or, best of all, if possible, to the fortress.[3]

[3] Is the fable of the Pied Piper more than a fable? Mr. Heywood, of Corby, England, a ratcatcher by profession, obtains sensational results through a secret weapon. Emulating the medieval Pied Piper, he lures rats out of their holes by making a special sound on a whistle he has. The rats, as they come out, run over a contact poison and are soon dead.

Zoopsychologists have given thought to this interesting phenomenon. Their conclusion has been that it is a territorial defense reaction, the owning rats coming out to see what intruder dares to make these defiant noises at the entrance of their holes. But there is no question that Heywood's customers think he is a magician.

✓

Between Species

✓

THUS far we have studied the behavior of animals toward their fellows, but it is obvious that animals of different species have many chances to meet, to conflict, to devour each other, to exploit or even help each other. At any rate, the various species rarely ignore one another.

✓ THE HUNTER AND HIS PREY

One of the most common situations is that of cat and mouse, of hunter and hunted. One can easily imagine the number of questions which can be asked on this account. Here again, we will have to make a rather restrictive selection.

Let us first see whether an animal knows instinctively how to get away from one that is lying in wait and means to kill him.

A German ornithologist by the name of Heinroth pointed out that many birds react to the sight of a predator in the sky. These reactions differ—call of alarm, winged flight, perfect immobility—but all are due to the presence of the bird of prey. Heinroth, who ran a zoo, was able to make numerous observations; among them he recorded that certain birds showed marked fear reactions when there was no bird of prey at all in the sky but only some harmless martins.

The truth then suddenly appeared to him: predators and martins had one thing in common, the shortness of their necks. Other researchers were able to confirm this hypothesis when experimental ethology developed. Using cardboard silhouettes, they tried to provoke fear reactions in various birds, and they succeeded when they employed short-necked silhouettes. ·

It is possible to achieve similar results by using an ambiguous silhouette made up of two spread wings and two extensions, one short and the other long. If this silhouette moves with the long excrescence forward, it looks somewhat like a goose and provokes no reaction. On the other hand, if we reverse the direction, it looks much more like a predator, and the fear reactions set in immediately.

It was suggested that such silhouettes might be used as scarecrows to protect especially precious vegetation, collections of plants, or selective sowings. Decoys thus suspended from small balloons did prove very effective, and were it not for the question of cost this method might well become widespread.

In other cases, it is not the sight organ which is important but the sense of smell; many mollusks react to the approach of one of their fiercest enemies, the starfish, by fleeing as fast as possible. But it is strange to note that those species of starfish known to be exclusively herbivorous cause no fear reaction whatsoever.

The scallops' behavior is the most amusing. These mollusks long since invented jet propulsion. By rapidly closing the valves of their shells, they expel water in a process not unlike that of a rocket, moving forward in speedy jumps. The approach of a starfish causes a headlong flight of whole shoals of scallops, but here again only the truly dangerous ones have this effect.

When we discuss bats, we will see that some millers are highly

A hare running for its life.
—Photo René Gacond

sensitive to the ultrasonic waves emitted by these animals. It has also been noted that salmon refuse to go upstream in any river which leads toward a mammal. The smell or the taste of water in which a living mammal has bathed is an unquestionable repellent to the salmon, a fish of which bears are known to be very fond.

The struggle for life, the contest between species, sometimes takes on a tragic aspect.

From the 300,000 eggs laid by a carp, or the astronomical numbers of eggs laid by insects, only an infinitesimal number of adults will grow.

Birds, on this score, are somewhat privileged characters, and yet out of 100 eggs there develop only 8 to 18 adults, depending on the species.

◢ ARE THERE HEREDITARY ENEMIES?

The question might be put the other way. Does the preying animal really know his victim?

As against man who often kills haphazardly, most animals know exactly what prey they want, and they do not attack other animals systematically. Boulet has shown that the cuttlefish shows no aggressiveness toward a black disc one and a half inches in diameter which is moved along the glass of its aquarium, whereas it will try to attack a dead crab of the same size presented to it in the same conditions. But if we take off several of the crab's claws, the cuttlefish shows only minimal interest. When the crab becomes clawless, the attack turns into flight.

Finally, if shown a photograph of a crab, the fish essays some tentative attacks, but with much less assurance than when the crab is three-dimensional.

Poorly interpreted experiments a few decades ago led many people to the conclusion that the cat did not know the mouse instinctively and that he needed his mother to teach him that the mouse was edible.

It seems, however, that he does not have to be taught to kill a mouse and that, as soon as he is old enough to do it, he will jump on the first mouse he meets. But if, in infancy, he is brought up in the company of a mouse, he will learn to love it and will never become a mouse hunter.

A study of animal gastronomy shows that certain hunting animals have a very pronounced taste for certain types of game. This may play a considerable role in effecting a balance among the species.

For instance, the cat prefers the black rat to the sewer rat, which is certainly to the latter's advantage. Frogs very gladly eat butterflies, while toads rarely do, and rennets virtually never.

Among insects, many are specialized hunters, going after only one kind of prey. The pompilid wasp, a kind of hymenopteridae, hunts only spiders. There is also a ferocious bee hunter among the wasps: in Germany, it is known as the bee-wolf; France, being more pedantic, has given it the name of apivorous philanthid.[1]

Tinbergen, with some university students from the north of Holland, spent each summer, from 1930 to 1935, observing philanthids' activities. Among other facts, he tried to find out how this insect went about telling honey bees from the multitude of very similar animals found in the moors.

The philanthidae never make a mistake, and they can tell honey bees from solitary bees, which so often look so much like them, as well as from certain other diptera which look exactly like bees.

The visual acuteness of the philanthidae, like that of so many insects, is not very great, and it is quite certain that this insect cannot by sight tell the details which distinguish a bee from a drone or other syrphid.

Obviously, it was rather difficult to study the capture of the prey: how could the eyes follow a philanthid until it had decided to attack its prey? Tinbergen simplified the problem. He had noted that the hunter often let his prey fall and then found it again very easily on the ground. That being the case, it was much easier to capture a philanthid heavily weighted down with a corpse, to take it from him, and then study how he went about finding it again.

Various experiments demonstrated that the philanthid hunted with his sense of smell and that he could smell his way back to an invisible bee.

But, in nature, the behavior of the animal on the hunt appeared equally associated with the visual element. At times, Tinbergen had been able to observe philanthids creeping up on various insects,

[1] The word was created by linguists from the Greek *philos*, meaning friend, and another Greek word, *anthos*, meaning flower.

The odor of fish attracts the water beetle which does not use its enormous eyes to hunt.
A stickleback the victim of a deadly sting.

flying around them, and then losing interest when they turned out not to be bees.

Tinbergen, anxious to make a leisurely observation of this insect's hunting habits, hung dead bees from a thread and then waited. For quite a while, nothing happened; the philanthids passed nearby without deigning to take an interest in the treats being offered them. Then there was a gust of wind, the dead bees started to sway, and a philanthid immediately went after one of the corpses. Just as if he were hunting a live animal, he grabbed the cadaver, plunged his stinger into its neck, and tried to carry it off.

Tinbergen had just discovered a new fact concerning the philanthids. He had also brought to light an absolutely general law of instinctive behavior, that of the independence of sequences from each other. Animal behavior can be divided into sequences separate from each other, during which quite different stimuli will be necessary. A motionless body smelling like a bee has something evocative for the philanthid in the second phase of his hunt (when he has killed and just lost his prey), but the same stimulus has no meaning at all for the philanthid who is still on the lookout for prey. First he must have a moving object of approximately the size of a bee and impregnated with the bee's smell.

There is even a corollary. If we wave a decoy in the air, a little bee-sized ball of cotton impregnated with bee-odor, the philanthid will be attracted; he will rapidly take the object between his legs, but as opposed to what happened with the bee's corpse, he will not try to sting it at all. At this stage, there must be tactile stimuli involved, for the hairiness of the bee very probably constitutes a stimulus which is indispensable in this chain of sequences.

It would, moreover, be possible to find almost equally conclusive examples in the behavior of the higher animals. Very often, men attacked by large felines have been spared by their aggressors if they remained completely motionless.

The mimetic capacities of certain animals have caused much ink to flow and would deserve extensive study. Animals have a thousand disguises so as to escape their adversaries. Some blend into the surrounding colors; others imitate a leaf or a twig; still others take on mottles or stripes. Those which know that they are not edible dress themselves up in the brightest colors as if to advertise to their enemies the unattractiveness of their flesh. But this dodge, it would seem, has also been used by some very tasty animals who adopt the bright advertising colors in the hope of discouraging gastronomes.

These phenomena are fascinating to study, especially since the allegations that these disguises serve no purpose have been punctured by experiment.

The simulation of death is a defensive weapon very often used by animals. A great number of insects can play dead very realistically; snakes do likewise; and mammals are sometimes real virtuosos at this game.

The Virginia opossum (or possum [2]) seems particularly gifted: in case of hopeless danger, he rolls over on his side, tongue hanging out, eyes closed, and muscles completely relaxed. Heartbeat and respiration become almost undetectable, and he can remain in this state for several minutes.

As for Renard, the fox, we know from the medieval romance which bears his name that he is capable of doing it as well.

Birds have an even more unusual defense system. The hatcher, or mother in charge of a brood, in order to turn away the interest of an enemy, imitates the actions of a wounded animal.

For a long time, the tale of the bird pretending to be wounded and hopping along with a hanging wing in order to coax a fox or cat away from its nest was considered by zoologists to be totally ridiculous. However, modern ornithologists have proved the credibility of Aristotle and the many hunters who have claimed to have observed this. We now have photographs and moving pictures enough to convince even the most incredulous. Birds as diverse as ducks, ostriches, plovers, or sparrows have been thus meticulously observed.

Sanders, an American ornithologist, tells of one day seeing a duck swimming along the edge of a lake, followed by her entire family. A bird of prey appeared in the sky, and, while the ducklings scampered for shelter among the reeds, the duck put on a startling performance. Her wing hanging, she appeared incapable of handling herself and turned in circles as might do a seriously wounded bird.

[2] From which we, of course, get the English phrase "to play possum." Tr. Note.

The bird of prey ignored the ducklings who were taking shelter and went after the she-duck. The latter, picking up speed at the last moment, made a straight line for a bush overhanging the shore. But then, noticing that two of her brood were still not safely sheltered, she headed into the water again to repeat her cripple act, which once again deceived the predator.

Advances made in descriptive zoology have upset many preconceived ideas of the relations between species.

We now know that Scottish deer often eat frogs and that the aquatic musk deer of tropical Africa is largely carnivorous.

There is also a common spider in the south of India known to live in water and eat small fish.

And one could mention fishing bats and many other "nonconformist" species, the diets of which seem to us a far cry from what general opinion would imagine them to be.

Eat or be eaten is a basic law of the universe, but there are more subtle forms of this struggle; at times even, instead of conflict, there may be mutual advantages.

PARASITES AND COMMENSALS

Parasitism has always been an intriguing question. In the days when the concept of a universe created once and for all time was accepted by most scientists and theologians, the problem of intestinal worms bothered many minds. After all, Adam, created in a state of perfection, could not have had any and, if they adjusted to their life at a later date, this would mean that there had been some changes made! Moreover, there exist all degrees between parasitism which is damaging to the host and cohabitation with mutual advantages.

Commensalism is the form of life in which the two species are useful to each other. In this category are to be found the many birds who accompany large animals: bovines or crocodiles. These birds eat off their host by clearing him of parasitic insects or, in the case of the crocodiles, of the excess food which remains in his jaw. In no case are they absolutely dependent on each other, and their association is purely voluntary.

A much more interesting example is the association of a crus-

From one end of the zoological scale to the other, mutual understanding is possible.

The crocodile and the parakeet: it could be the title of a fable by La Fontaine.—Photo Steve Henty

tacean, the pagurian or hermit crab, and the sea anemone. This happens frequently, for many shell collectors have noticed shells adorned with an anemone cohabiting with the owner who is inside. Sometimes the union of these two animals can be accidental. The anemone just happens to land on the shell, but in that case the association does not usually last very long. Sometimes, the association, though optional, becomes much closer and displays a definitely "voluntary" character. When the hermit crab grows and has to move to a larger shell, he takes his companion in his claws and transports it to his new home.

Lastly, in a final group, there are those which simply can no longer live apart, the shapes of the two associates literally merging into each other; at the extreme, the pagurian no longer even needs his shell, which becomes reabsorbed, and he lives inside the actinia. In the opinion of those who study them, these associations are advantageous to both partners. The hermit crabs no longer have to change habitats each time they grow larger; they may make their homes in areas where no shells are to be found, such as the great deep; and the sea anemones are delighted to feed on the remains of their associates' feasts.

Another, more obscure, example is supplied by the association of a small fish, known as the clown fish, with sea anemones. In this case, the sea anemone is stationary, and the fish moves freely away. At the least danger, however, he comes to seek refuge in the tentacles of his protector and, moreover, does not hesitate to pick up stray bits of food right in her gastric cavity. Nevertheless, the slightest contact with an actinia is fatal to any other fish and, even if we admit that the actinia is able to recognize its familiar friend or even to find pleasure in his company to the point of trying to spare him, the fact still remains that there must be some kind of protective mechanism.

How is this immunity acquired? In the case of the fish, just as in that of the hermit crab, we can present only hypotheses. Yet we are certain that such immunity exists, for the blood of hermit crabs carrying actinia can be employed as an antidote to the venom secreted by their associates.

Apart from these problems which are of such interest to psychologists, it remains to be determined how such unions could ever have come about. Either the fish had an immunity from the start and the actinia got used to his presence, or else, as is more likely there was no immunity to begin with, but the clown fish was able in one way or another, to "tame" the monster.

✓ THE ART OF BEING BORNE

Among the many gradations between parasitism and mutual help which we mentioned, there is one rather curious form of behavior generally known as phoresia, or the ability that certain animals have to get others to carry them for a wide variety of reasons.

Very often, these reasons seem quite obscure. An arachnidian living in a nest of bumblebees and feeding on their excrement will apparently from time to time take a pleasure flight on the back of one of his hosts.

Sometimes such transportation allows a parasite to go from one host to another; the buffalo louse seems in this way to be carried from one animal to another by a fly. And we all know about the remora fish which latch on to the bellies of sharks with suction grips.

✓ DEMENTIAL PARASITISM

This brings us to fullfledged parasitism.

It should be noted that this way of life is adopted only by certain species of animals: there are, for instance, no spiders, echinoderms, or sponges which are parasites, whereas there are no trematode (fluke) or cestoda (tape) worms to which parasitism is alien.

It is impossible to draw up in a few lines the full picture of parasitism, and we must be satisfied to note only a few examples selected among the most remarkable ones. For instance, there is a threadworm (or nematode) which lives in the urinary bladder of the rat; at least, the female does, for the male, which is smaller, uses a parasitism once removed and spends his life in the female's uterus. The trematodes, which include the flukes, work out their survival through a highly complicated cycle. The lungfluke takes as its first host a water snail, from which it emigrates to inhabit a crab, and finally terminates its career in a human. Another of the trematodes starts its evolution in a fresh-water mussel, then selects a herbivorous fish, and ends its days in a flesh-eating fish.

In some cases, the specificity is very great, meaning that the parasite can select only a very well-defined host; but in other cases the possibilities of adaptation are quite broad. Within the same family one always finds common parasites; we are subject to approximately the same ones as the anthropoid apes.

There are, of course, riddles before which zoologists remain perplexed, such as certain sea fish, the boces, whose parasitic fauna is typically that of a batrachian.

This aspect of the life of the species presents many questions and problems which are insoluble. It is sufficient for us to know that they exist and that this aspect of evolution, even though it may seem regressive to us, belongs in our view of the living world if we want that view to be comprehensive.

ꜰ WAR

Having looked at individuals, we must now discuss the relations between groups of individuals. The power balance between species is not a stable thing. Following given circumstances, animals which have been restricted to a certain part of the globe may invade the entire earth. Examples of such invasions are numerous; in France, there have been invasions by the phylloxera, the potato beetle, the Chinese crab, the San Jose louse, and the *hotu* fish.

In many cases it is not proper to refer to a struggle between the species, even though there may be favorable or unfavorable effects on the fauna as a whole when a new species starts to proliferate. But, sometimes, there is really an active invasion; the intruders set about killing and destroying. This was the case of the Argentinian ant which, in certain islands, destroyed all pre-existing species of ants.

ꜰ THE DESPOT RAT

This also happens with rats. Wars between rats take place unbeknownst to us in our very cellars and attics.

The oldest denizen is the black rat. But he is not really fully entitled to this distinction, for he himself only invaded Europe in the Middle Ages. He was probably the one mainly responsible for the great epidemics of plague. His enemy, who has almost eliminated him, is the brown rat, also known as sewer rat or surmulot (or Norway rat). Coming from Asia, like most invaders, over the plains which have carried so many invasions from the paleolithic age to our own days, the sewer rat invaded France in the eighteenth century. The first of his kind was seen in Paris in 1793. That year saw the end of two reigns, that of the Bourbons and that of the black rat.

The reason for the latter defeat is to be found in a rather mysterious law which governs the relations between almost similar species. Very often, when two such species come into conflict, one wins out over the other, without it being a question of physical strength. The rabbit thus would drive out the hare, the roebuck would do likewise to the chamois, and it seems that the occasional Asian lions still to be found in one region of India are in a position of inferiority to the tiger.

The only way out left to the species which is the underdog in this conflict seems to be the colonization of areas disregarded by the adversary. The black rat therefore survives in places where the sewer rat cannot or does not want to live any longer. He becomes king of the attics while cellars become the undisputed domain of the sewer rat.

In southern France, outside the large cities, there is still quite a density of black rats, whereas they are no longer to be found in the north, especially along rivers and canals.

This war between the rats has been going on for a very long time, but it is by no means certain that the outcome has been decided, and in certain countries, like Germany and Switzerland, the black rat seems to be gaining the upper hand once again, according to certain reports.

COEXISTENCE

Subtle factors which, in our eyes, appear to be imponderables, govern these balances. Favoring now one species, now the other, they can bring it either ruin or victory. Fortunately, however, such wars to extermination are not the general rule.

We have already discussed the territories which are so jealously protected by their proprietors against animals of their own species.

These territories, on the other hand, may be open to any number of animals of other species.

There are pyramids of territories within a given region. Thus, within the lion's vast territory there will be the territories of various medium-sized herbivorous species, and a great number of territories belonging to rodents, and so on.

A census taken by Leopold in Arizona, starting with a territory of approximately half a square mile belonging to a coyote, showed the presence of two owls, two falcons, 15 skunks, 25 horned animals, 80 hares and rabbits, and close to 20,000 mice and other rodents.

And, of course, in this type of enumeration, there is generally not included the teeming mass of invertebrates, insects or worms, which are the base of the pyramid.

The affinities of species for each other are very strange. Thus, in winter, flocks are made up of various species of sparrows, yet titmice will allow no stranger among them. In the case of shore birds, the avocets are almost as inflexible, but they will put up with the presence of stilts.

It is very difficult to speak of adaptation in the case of some animal behavior. While it may seem perfectly well adjusted in a given situation, it can in fact be so rigid, so unadaptable to anything new, that the term adjustment itself becomes ludicrous.

We find an example of this in the behavior of the muskoxen of the Arctic. These animals, when attacked, form a circle, the young taking refuge in the center and the adults making a rampart of their horns. This tactic is obviously excellent against attack by a wolf, but it is disastrous against a man armed with a gun. The last of the muskoxen owe their survival only to very rigorous legal protection. On the other hand, the partridge, which has unquestionably learned to adapt the length of its flight to the range of firearms, shows up on this score as a much better adapted animal.

An animal is never really a solitary creature. The species inevitably meet, and they either come into conflict or join together in one way or another.

✓

Mutual Help among Animals

✓

AN American ornithologist living in Costa Rica, Alexander F. Skutch, has devoted thirty years of his life to the study of mutual help between birds. In a recent publication which collects his own observations and those of his colleagues, he amazed specialists in the animal psyche by proving that there were certain birds which could actually be called "assistants."

From what is now known, such assistant birds exist in over 130 different species. An assistant is any bird which on certain occasions will help another who is neither his mate nor one of his young, for mutual help among members of a family is an everyday occurrence.

This assistance can be found in many different circumstances, especially when a nest has to be built or the young have to be fed.

San Francisco Bay cormorants hunt shoals of fish by forming into irregular battlelines. Some fly at a low altitude, while others dive and swim for great distances under water. Whichever they may do, they keep their distances and advance at the same rate without trying to take advantage of each other individually, always acting in terms of what is best for the group.

The help that birds most often give each other, however, is a warning of the approach of an enemy. Such assistance, to be sure, can exist between animals of the same species as it can between those of different species. Sometimes it is compensated for with reciprocal help, sometimes not.

⌄ SENTRIES AND NURSES

The warning that a neighbor gives at the approach of danger is a particularly effective and widespread service, but it is not of major interest to us, because it would seem much too difficult to prove its intentional character. If it seems quite certain that the warning cry of the blackbird or the jay informs all the woodland birds of the approach of man, there is no basis for claiming on that account that they act as assistants.

The same cannot be said for mutual aid in the food department. Such help may be given not only to baby birds, but also to crippled birds or others who, for one reason or another, are unable to feed themselves. In this connection, in a colony of white pelicans, observers found an old bird virtually incapable of moving, who, demonstrably, would have had no chance of surviving if his companions had not taken the trouble to feed him. Likewise, there was seen in a colony of brown loons a bird that had lost a wing in an accident; this bird, also, was able to survive thanks only to the food furnished him by his fellows.

Among mammals, many elephant hunters have told how these pachyderms try to come to the assistance of a wounded congener. All these descriptions agree, and, moreover, films that have been made show us how it happens: two friends take their places at the wounded elephant's right and left, with others sometimes reinforcing them and still another pushing from behind. One hunter saw a set of "stretcher-bearers" raise a wounded animal in this way along a steep bank to a height of almost 50 feet.

There is also the story of the crow who passed food out through the bars of his cage to a black vulture flying free on the outside. It is true that in this specific case the crow's behavior may have had other motives than alleged altruism. It is known that birds belonging to the corvine family are in the habit of including a food offering in the ceremonial which precedes mating. Under these conditions, it can be wondered whether this crow, well-fed but lonely, had not been sexually attracted by the only black bird living near him. Skutch, in his book, propounds this very likely explanation, but he points out at the same time that there are other facts which are more difficult to explain.

Among certain birds the need to devote themselves to others is so strong that they will even feed fish.—Photo Rapho

﹖ ALTRUISM?

For instance, a cardinal was observed one day feeding a gold-fish. The bird was seen doing this several times, and it was possible to get photographs of it; the cardinal perched on the edge of the basin and held in his beak a morsel which he would then transfer to the mouth of the goldfish. A possible explanation of this action is that the bird, having somehow had his brood annihilated, and seeing the open mouth of the reddish fish, had automatically responded by supplying food, a need of which he had been cheated.

Then there is the case of a bird and a bear. The indicator bird is very fond of honey but is afraid to confront bees. When he has found a hive, he seeks out a bear and goes into an extraordinary act, flying about and singing at the top of his lungs. What is even more amazing is that the bear seems to understand and readily takes off in the direction indicated by the bird.

Once at the hive, the bear makes short work of getting the honey out without paying attention to the stings which scarcely penetrate his fur and hide. And the bird is quite content to pick up the crumbs of this feast.

This bird, quite common in the Balkans, leads men to honey in the same manner, by indicating the location of wild swarms in the forest. The bee hunters always make sure to leave a bit of their find as a reward for the volunteer guide.

Another curious type of mutual aid is that given the remora by the shark. In the Caribbean, on his second trip to the West Indies, Christopher Columbus was struck by the sight of the strange remora, to the point that he had the shipboard scribe take down the essential characteristics of this animal.

The Romans attributed extraordinary power to this fish: they believed that if it latched on to a ship, it would be able to stop its course. The death of the Emperor Caligula was blamed on a remora, which, having held back his speedy galley, had separated it from the rest of the fleet.

In point of fact, the reasons for the curious morphological transformation which took place in the remora to bring into existence the suction cup under its head, and especially the reasons which cause the shark to tolerate the presence of this cumbersome guest, remain a mystery.

There is a kind of mutual help among ants. Often, one will see several of them get together to move some particularly voluminous prey. Chauvin, a few years ago, wanted to find out whether when two ants join to move a load there is a noticeable saving of time over the same job being done by one alone. From his observations, such a saving can go as high as 50 per cent. But the saving lessens proportionately when three workers work at the same task, and there is no further saving at all if as many as four labor together.

Mutual help, if the term is justified in describing such behavior on the part of ants, is therefore limited to a very small number of workers, and beyond that number total anarchy seems to set in.

Another method of mutual help which is rather surprising is what might be described as the "nursery."

Among a great number of birds, most often those who make their nests at ground level and live in colonies, one can observe institutions of this kind. When the young are able to leave the nest under their own power, but before they can dream of having an independent life of their own, the parents have to keep a careful watch over them, which is a difficult task. This could interfere with the success of their hunting or fishing if birds of many different species did not resort to a method of collective supervision. In this way, we find chicks born of different parents playing under the watchful eye of only one or several adults. It has been possible to make very precise records of such nurseries among penguins and ducks as well as flamingoes. While the young may appear to be lost in the crowd and all mixed up, their parents recognize them, and, come mealtime, they feed only their own progeny, turning a deaf ear to the appeals of all the others.

A study of the facts, as well as a bit of thought, shows that group feeding would be hard to do, as Skutch has so correctly pointed out; unless the chicks were trained to feed each in his turn, the biggest and most aggressive ones would always be the best-fed and the weakest ones could not fail to die of inanition. Though we know that within one brood the weak ones are certainly at a disadvantage, this cannot result in the disappearance of entire families. This system would be one way to allow the method of natural selection to operate, but there are plenty of other occasions in the life of the young bird when he comes face to face with this selection process.

It may be noted in passing that, with some birds, the nestlings do come each in turn to get fed. This is what happens with the king-fisher. The brood is hidden in a very dark haven, and the parents would be hard put there to tell one baby from another. But the problem never arises, for the young kingfishers make a circle within the nest and the one who is closest to the entryway simply opens his beak to receive his share. Then, the circle swings around one notch, another one is nearest, and he in turn has only to open his beak at the next appearance of the feeder.

In some circumstances, it happens that the young may be fed by birds who are not their parents. This has been noted in particular among numerous species of wild ducks. Orphaned ducklings simply join another family in which they are usually very well-received. A couple of parents may, moreover, adopt several orphaned broods, and Hochbaum tells of the case of one big-hearted duck who assumed responsibility for no less than 84 ducklings!

Among certain species, joint child-rearing has been carried even further.

Some cuckoos found in the United States, far from having the parasitic conduct of the European species, have on the contrary a highly developed social sense. There is one species in which the couples live together in groups on a common territory. At mating time, each couple may build its own nest, but it may also happen that the birds build only one communal nest in which all of the females lay their eggs. In some cases, the common nest is the abso-lute rule.

⁊ HELP GIVEN BY THE YOUNGER
GENERATIONS

Another very remarkable form of assistance: the help that the "big children" give their parents with the upbringing of belated broods. Here are a few examples: young coots are often fed by their elder siblings; a young pigeon is reported to have helped its mother hatch a second brood and then feed the youngsters.

Among certain martins, similar cases of assistance have been observed, but it was not always young birds who were offering to

The young cuckoo, a lazy drone, wears out its adopted mother, who breathlessly races around to feed this egotistical youngster.

—Photo François Merlet

help; sometimes it was old ones or even, without our having any way of knowing what their motives might be, quite normal-appearing adults. Only one week after having made their first flight, fledgling swallows are ready to help their parents build a nest or feed a second brood.

Skutch saw one young Mexican jay help his parents. He brought building materials for the nest and then food for the setting hen; after that he helped feed the newly-hatched chicks and stood guard over the nest even more vigilantly than did the parents.

Even more extraordinary are the tales of mutual help between animals belonging to different species. Some birds in this way take charge of young which are not of their species or come to the help of parents who have overly large families.

Here again, the observations have been innumerable.

⌐ SOME MYSTERIES OF LOVE

A male towhee, whose young had just flown off to start living their own lives, put himself at the disposal of a family of cardinals and took it upon himself to help them feed their brood.

After having brought up her own progeny, a female blackbird continued for about three weeks to offer food to all the birds within range of her nest. Several of them accepted the proffered food, in particular an adult robin redbreast.

We also know of a male goose who attached himself to a domesticated duck and her thirteen ducklings and took care of this family as if it were his own. It would become tiresome to go on with the list, for, as we said, such acts have been noted in 130 different species of birds.

Although no systematic study has been made of mammals, we know that the bitch adopting kittens or the she-cat nursing young hedgehogs are common situations, and this leads us to the instances of adoption of human infants or small children by animals.

⌐ THE ENIGMA OF THE WOLF-CHILDREN

From the legendary tale of Romulus and Remus down to our own day, stories of wolf-children are legion. They should not really always be so called, for their foster parents have not necessarily been wolves. In 1661, deep in the heart of the Lithuanian forest, a child was discovered who had supposedly been raised by bears. And in 1671 another was found living under the care of only a few sheep.

In 1815, there was reported to be one living among pigs, and in 1946 a boy of 13 or 14 was discovered who had been raised by gazelles. The latter, who was captured by some hunters, turned out to be absolutely impervious to any psychic reeducation.

As far as wolf-children are concerned, they are particularly numerous in India. The most recent one, so far as we know, was the one found in January 1957 in the jungle of Uttar Pradesh.

But the most famous without question are two little girls, Amala and Kamala. They were found by Reverend Singh and a Hindu hunter southeast of Calcutta in October 1920, in the company of adult wolves and two cubs. Amala was not destined to outlive the first attempts at reeducation, but Kamala lived nine years longer with Reverend Singh, who succeeded, up to a point, in coaxing her across the gulf that separates the lupine psyche from the human.

This experiment was most useful for strengthening the arguments of advocates of environment as compared to heredity as the most important influence on a child. A specialist in child psychology, Arnold Gesell, even wrote an important book about the case.

But the truth of such stories has often been questioned by those who deem that tales of children adopted by wolves can exist only in the minds of imaginative novelists. It is quite true that Reverend Singh's tale has a number of contradictions in it, and even some flagrant untruths, but this is not sufficient reason to deny the possibility that a wild animal might adopt a human baby. The many examples that we have just cited would tend on the contrary to prove that adoption among animals is much more widespread than anyone would have believed.

CHAPTER IV

ʹ

The Social Animal

ʹ

IN dealing with animal societies, one somewhat gets the feeling of discovering a new continent in the universe we are exploring. Social life adds a new dimension to the animal, to the point that the hive, the ant hill, or the herd seem almost the result of a mutation. Yet, all the intermediary degrees exist between the social animal and the solitary one.[1]

What is the social animal?

The answers may vary according to who gives them, but we will take essentially one given by a specialist in social animals, Grassé. In his view, the criteria of the social state must be objective, and to understand them, it is especially necessary first to define what we mean by interattraction and group effects.

ʹ MECHANICS OF INTERATTRACTION

Interattraction is quite easy to characterize. When animals form a group, there may be two causes: attraction through an external stimulus or mutual attraction among the animals themselves. A classic example: bees crowded on to a saucer containing traces of jam or honey are attracted by external stimulation, and in no case could this be considered a social phenomenon. On the other hand, bees, sleeping separately in a closed box, have a tendency imme-

---

[1] We have to recognize that each of our classifications, so convenient for learning, so easy for teaching, really only coincides approximately with reality. We often have the feeling that we are trying to put into the same drawer various things which rather belong in two separate drawers simultaneously.

diately upon awakening to form groups of several individuals, and these groups then merge into one including all the individuals.

The interattraction of bees was studied in France by Lecomte, who discovered that worker bees are attracted to each other by the low-frequency vibrations they emit and by their own odor, but that attraction does not take on an effective scale unless the social group is rather significant, that is, includes at least fifty-odd individuals.

Equally spectacular examples of interattraction can be discovered among all social insects, and even among those considered subsocial. The cockroach and the banana weevil, for instance, have gregarious tendencies which come to the fore in many circumstances.

⟨ THE GROUP EFFECT

Another criterion of the social state is represented by the group effect which results in a noticeable change in the psychology, the physiology, or even the morphology of the animal, according to whether he is alone or in a group.

Migratory grasshoppers appear to us in very differing aspects. The lone grasshopper is greenish, whereas the social grasshopper is black and red. For a long time, it was believed there were two different species until Uvarov demonstrated that it was social grouping which transformed the *locusta danica* into the *locusta migratoria*.

After the usual period of amazement and disbelief, biologists undertook the study of other migratory acrididae, and in each case found similar phenomena. A few years before the last war, Chauvin studied the pilgrim cricket from this viewpoint. In addition to noting the changes resulting from the grouping phenomenon, he also tried to bring out the physiological mechanisms involved. There are three different stages to be observed here: successively, the gregariousness of the larva, that of the adult, and sexual gregariousness.

The larvae change colors according to whether they are in a group or separated. The sight of their congeners seems to play an essential role in this, for the green larva placed within a group of black larvae, but isolated from them inside a hermetic glass container, changes color as if it were more intimately joining the group. Visual stimulation therefore seems to be enough, but it is not irreplaceable: in total darkness, a green larva will also turn black on contact with the others; in that case it is the antennae which play the important role. In nature, obviously, these two stimuli work together.

Adult crickets undergo similar influences. The males, lemon-yellow when living in a group, remain grayish if alone. In this case, antenna contact is required to bring about the transformation. The insect placed in a glass bottle in the midst of the group will generally remain gray if his antennae have been cut off, and at any rate the yellow coloration will come only with great delay, probably through the intervention of another receiver: perhaps as a result of olfactory stimulation at a very short distance.

Sexual gregariousness is the tendency noted in females to produce larvae which have less and less solitary characteristics in proportion to the length of time the males have cohabited with them.

It should not be assumed, just because we took it as a criterion, that coloration alone differentiates the solitary cricket from the gregarious ones. They do not share the same degree of activity, the same size, the same appetite, the same metabolism, or even the same life span.

Such group effects, more or less pronounced, exist in a large number of animals. They are particularly noticeable in those insects which belong to higher societies, but they are difficult to study because here the isolated animal does not survive very long. This in itself can be considered a group effect; the animal can be seen to die of separation from his partners just as a cell dies when it is separated from the body to which it belongs.

These two criteria will now allow us to delve into animal societies. But since there is no connection between the various social phenomena, it is more rational first to observe what takes place among the invertebrates before considering superior animal societies.

First, we find those animals which form uncoordinated groupings. They have a mutual attraction for each other, but their associations are of a temporary and optional nature and among these animals there is no coordination of movement or activity. The group, as such, shows no aggressiveness toward outsiders. This is true of kitchen roaches for instance.

Then there are simple coordinated groupings. These are still optional groups open to outsiders; no collective building is to be found in them, but there is some coordination of movement. The larvae of sawflies, which move about in quasi-military formation, are a valid example of these groupings.

Finally come the inferior societies characterized by collective building but having no division of labor or complex organization. They are often temporary and remain relatively open. The procession caterpillars, which spin their nests in pine trees, belong to this category. We should perhaps also include the social spiders, although their societies may be more complex than is generally believed.

This brings us to the higher societies.

⁊ THE GREAT ANIMAL SOCIETIES

These are to be found exclusively in two orders of insects: the *isoptera,* which include termites, and the *hymenoptera,* particularly full of social insects: ants, bees, and wasps. These societies, generally quite exclusive, are characterized by the intense interattraction which unites their members. Division of labor is very highly developed, and a collective construction shelters the colony.

Let us examine, as an example, what happens in a beehive. Within the hive, three different kinds of individuals may be found. In the first place, there is the queen, who for a long time was thought to be a king. It was only in the seventeenth century that her true identity was discovered and it was learned that she was the exclusive mother of the whole colony.

Then, there are the males. While there is only one queen, there may be as many as a thousand or more males. Their existence is ephemeral, and once the fertilization season is over they will be summarily executed by the workers. These killers are the great mass of the colony: they have been known to number up to 40,000 or 50,000. They are actually females, but their atrophied ovaries make them into asexual beings. The workers do not all have the same tasks within the hive, and there is a very strict division of labor. The different activities are carried out by workers who are absolutely identical morphologically, in contrast to what happens among termites and ants, where there are various categories of individuals, often very different from each other.

Among bees, the division of labor is made according to age. Immediately after birth, the young worker is a cleaner; then she becomes a distributor or a storer—that is to say, she receives the

Whether an individual in a society or a cell in the superorganism, the bee becomes solitary at harvest time.—Photo Holmes-Lebel

food brought from the outside and places it within the cells of the honeycomb. Toward the sixth day, she turns into a nurse. Her feeding glands reach their maximum development and now start to secrete the well-known royal jelly, which feeds the very young worker larvae as well as the queen larvae. This stage lasts only a short time and, after the tenth day, the worker becomes a waxer. Then her wax glands atrophy in turn, and, about the twentieth day, the bee is ready to go into the outside world as a collector in search of the raw materials required for the activities of the colony.

The court attending the queen bee is made up of bees of greatly varying ages. A Scottish biologist studied this problem through the device of a glass-fronted hive and individually marked bees.

It was thus noted that the workers who fed the queen bee were between one and eleven days old, whereas those who come to inspect her with their antennae vary in age from a few hours to 36 days.

The time table of bee development, as Roesch drew it up some decades ago, is a bit oversimplified. In reality, things are less defined and more flexible.

Roesch himself demonstrated this by carrying out the following experiment: he split a colony in two, putting all the inside bees into one of the new hives and all the collectors into the other. That is easier to do than to explain. The two new colonies thus formed each had larvae which had to be fed, but the one had no nurses and the other no collectors. Very quickly, the two populations reacted to the situation. In the colony that had only collectors, a part of its members, no doubt the youngest of the bees, retrogressed two stages to the point where their atrophied glands developed again. In the other colony, a certain number of waxers skipped stages and became very expert collectors at an age when normally they should not have been leaving the warm darkness of the hive.

Guards also appear in some instances. This is not an obligatory stage, and many bees by-pass it. But at certain times of the year, when there is a danger of attack, some of the workers, before becoming collectors or even alternating with this task, do the work of guards posted as sentries at the entrance to the hive so they can drive off any marauders.

♪ A FASCINATING HYPOTHESIS: THE HYPERORGANISM

Such a degree of organization, along with the fact that a bee isolated from its kind, like a termite, lives only a very short time, brings up this question: can we compare the whole bee colony to an organism and should each individual be looked upon as one cell of this superorganism?

This idea was applied to domesticated bees a few years ago by Chauvin. Thus, in studying the overall functions of the hive, it could be seen that they have little in common with those of individual bees. Among other things, the hive breathes in a strange way; its internal atmosphere, heavy with carbon dioxide, is sometimes very quickly renewed: the "ventilators," by sweeping the air out with their wings, play the part of a lung. Its thermogenesis is also very interesting. The individual bee has no heat control mechanism, but the hive maintains a high temperature of around 68 degrees in winter and in summer struggles to avoid overheating. Circulation is carried on by the ceaseless exchange of food, which keeps numerous substances, like veritable hormones, on the move within the hive.

A whole series of other discoveries supports this theory of the superorganism which is now considered a very valid hypothesis, whereas for a long time it had seemed merely a mental concept. From the point of view of the superorganism, one should not attribute the startling psychic manifestations of the bee to the nervous system of each individual insect, but rather to that of the hive as a whole, which is much greater in scope and complexity.

Certain specialists believe that there are superorganisms even far more complex than the beehive. Let us look at the ants.

Everyone knows of the red woods ant, whose domes, built of twiglets, shelter sizable populations: sometimes there are more than a million inhabitants under one dome. A Belgian naturalist, Father Raignier, studied a great number of these nests and, to his great surprise, came across an extraordinary anomaly. In all known cases, the ants of two separate colonies, if they belong to the same species, are enemies. Brought face to face, the ant swarms of the same woods attack each other ferociously. Yet one day, Father Raignier discovered within the same woods a network of several tens of ant hills whose inhabitants all lived together in perfect harmony. This network of federated nests was connected by some six miles of paths and lived off some 75 acres.

Stammer discovered such a federation in Germany. It included 58 main ant hills and 31 secondary ones. These federations are quite rare, it would seem, but recently some French entomologists, wanting to study such associations, discovered the existence of authentic commerce between ants of different species. By feeding a colony of ants a sugar syrup containing radioisotopes, Chauvin, Courtois, and Lecomte discovered that not only was there spreading of the radio-activity to sister colonies, but that exchanges had also taken place with a different species, albeit a very closely related one.

These federations of superorganisms are enough to send the mind reeling, for, with just a bit of imagination, one can conclude that their infrequency indicates that they are part of an evolution. From there to going along with the science fiction writers who see humanity some day submerged beneath an entomological tide is not so great a step.

˅ BEYOND THE INSECTS

Now we must turn to the societies of higher animals. Here again we find the somewhat ambiguous groupings already noted among the invertebrates. Fish, batrachians, and snakes do form groups, under certain circumstances. At times, there is unquestionably co-ordination of movement. Under this heading, we know of shoals of fish: herrings, sardines, and others. There are also shoals of sea snakes, and some of the rodent migrations probably fall within the category of coordinated groups.

Mass flights of birds are no less startling. For if they all follow a common direction under the impulse of external causes, their flight formations obey other imperatives. There have been many descriptions of the V-shaped flights of migratory birds. The position of the spearhead bird who leads the way for his teammates is particularly interesting. He does not stay continuously in the lead; when fatigue sets in, he drops back to the extreme rear of the formation, and another bird takes his place.

Beyond that, we find monogamous and polygamous families,

colonial societies, juxtapositions of families, and finally societies in the proper sense of the term. There are many fewer common characteristics among vertebrates than among insects, but we can name at least one: the pecking order.

⁊ SOCIAL HIERARCHIES

A Norwegian, Schjelderup-Ebbe, discovered this shortly before the 1914 war, while observing a poultry yard. Roosters and hens, as everyone knows, peck at each other. But this pecking is not done haphazardly. The cock is entitled to peck at all the hens, but if there is no cock, one of the hens inherits the privilege. A second one has the right to peck at all the others except the first, and so on down the line. There is a linear hierarchy, down from the alpha individual who has precedence over everyone and who gets to eat first, to the omega individual who is everybody's pecking-boy. This hierarchy is to be found repeated in many types of behavior.

The stability of the hierarchy constitutes a biological advantage. This was proven by Allee, who compared groups of hierarchically stable chickens with other groups in which the structure was periodically upset by the replacement of the alpha individual with an outsider. At the end of a few weeks, the weights of the members of the two types of groups showed marked differences. The chickens of the consistently structured groups fattened much more rapidly than the others.

In groupings that have several males, there is a sexual hierarchy. Scott, studying the American woodcock, found that the alpha male was responsible for 75 per cent of the fertilizing, his second in command for 13 per cent, and the other males in the group for only 3 per cent each. These remaining males, usually numbering four or five, also have the additional duty of protecting the females from the attentions of males who are outside the group. This hierarchy is usually very stable.

Among birds which observe matrimonial customs, there is an amusing rule. A new bride takes on the rank of her spouse. In jackdaw society, it is especially funny to see a young female, usually placed on the lowest rung of the hierarchy, suddenly lording it over a large part of the group by virtue of having been selected by a well-placed male.

Sometimes, these hierarchies are extremely complex. This is the case with bovines. Among buffaloes, and even among domestic cattle, triangular hierarchies have been observed. Alpha comes ahead of beta, who comes ahead of gamma, but he in turn is over alpha. More often, there are combinations of both linear and triangular hierarchies. But in most cases, alpha is not actually a part of such an arrangement and lords it over everyone in an incontestable manner—incontestable, but not necessarily undisputed, for, from time to time, the whole order is challenged.

Once a year, the kine who retain semi-wild customs have it out in battles which have become part of the folklore of certain regions. Before going to pasture, it is necessary to establish who will lead the herd. In wild life, this distinction is generally given to an old female, although this does not automatically give her the alpha rating.

According to Schein, the different stages of the establishing of the hierarchy among domestic cattle are the approach, the threat, and the physical contact which turns into a struggle, and which may of course lead to either defeat or victory. This struggle is made up of a series of rounds, separated from each other by rest periods which may last from a few seconds to five minutes. During the rest periods, the animals go about very peaceful occupations, such as grazing, for instance.

Deer, as well as elands and other antlered beasts, also meet to establish a new order of things by battle, but not necessarily once a year. Some males can maintain their supremacy for years without having to defend the title. Here the symbolic role of the antlers seems apparent, for an old deer still retains his primacy during the short time before the dropping-off of his horns, even though they would patently come off at the first blow.

In animal societies, abnormal individuals are very differently treated, according to the species. Penguins do not tolerate mutants within their groups; they fall on them violently and drive them away. On the other hand, among many other birds, mutants are not only tolerated but even given special attention. Albino females, for example, are often especially sought after by males.

Animal hierarchy is closely connected with physiological condition, and especially with certain hormones. Usually when there are both sexes in the group, the males hold all the leading places; but it is possible to bring a female up the social scale by giving her an injection of a certain quantity of male hormones. The social sequence may also depend, in part, on the territory. We have already discussed what its territory means to an animal. Even animals living together in groups sometimes show a preference for certain parts of the common territory. A chicken wants to keep her own place on the perch, for instance. This individual territory can significantly influence the hierarchical relationships.

Masure and Allee noted that a female alpha pigeon won all the fights when she was perched at the entrance to the cote. On the ground, on the other hand, she could never win. Even the domination of the males is not always absolute and sometimes we see strange reversals of position. The most famous is that of the budgerigars (undulating grass-parakeets). Apart from the mating season, the females dominate all the males. Even low caste females get to feed before the highest ranking of the males. But, during the mating season, this whole established order is turned upside down, and the rights of the male sex are never challenged by the females.

Just the opposite occurs among canaries, where the male, usually dominant, becomes subservient at mating time.

Pigeons live in a troop. They are social animals who do not do well in isolation. Physiological troubles appear in that case, which interfere with reproduction. In particular, the female ovary cannot form any eggs without the excitement provided by the sight of another pigeon, whether male or female. A simple mirror placed in the cage will be quite enough to start the normal ovulation process.

We stated previously that the hierarchical structures of animal societies were rarely challenged. Animals have ways of making their social status known. We will see, when we speak of animal language, that complex codes may exist. This method of displaying social rank saves a lot of time and avoids many fights between potential leaders. In the final analysis, animal societies are reasonable, and the time lost in internal struggles is negligible.

Mice have been observed on this score for very long periods: out of 65,000 minutes, only 821 minutes were given over to individual contacts and only 18 per cent of those to fighting. So, a mouse fights with its fellow citizens only one quarter of one per cent of its life, this study seems to say. Pigeons are more aggressive, and their score stands at about one per cent. Chimpanzees, in contradiction to what might be expected, do not expend more than two fifths of one per cent of their activity in fights.

Can we now escape the temptation to make comparisons with human societies? They quite naturally come to mind, and the stories our naturalists tell quickly remind us of our own experiences. Who among us does not recognize the chick of little social standing who turns arrogant after marrying well, or the pigeon who is lordly in her own favorite setting but loses face elsewhere?

In the same way, the behavior of the outsider who tries to get into the group, either by humbly assuming a rear rank, or by trying to grab the top spot right away, is reminiscent of much of human behavior.

Animal sociology, at least that of the vertebrates, is perhaps not so far away from the fundamentals of our own.

✓

An Outline of Plant Psychology

✓

AT the end of the eighteenth century, a German by the name of Sprengel [1] discovered that flowers had not been created for the sake of men, but for the sake of insects.

The flower and the insect are perfectly adapted to each other: the flower gives the sugar of its nectar and a food rich in proteins, its pollen; the insect assures survival in the vegetable kingdom by carrying the pollen from one flower to the other, thus accomplishing fertilization.

The first flowers appeared on the surface of the globe in the middle of the Mesozoic Age, or about 150,000,000 years ago. The earliest fossil pollens known to us come from water lilies and plants which closely resemble magnolias. At that time, the most efficient pollinating insects did not yet exist, and coleoptera no doubt took

---

[1] Sprengel's work is a magnificent example of what intuition can contribute to science. For it must be admitted that, however appealing his views, they were based on nothing precise, just as their logic was based neither on experiment nor on any knowledge of insect vision.

It was to be feared that the progress of science might leave nothing standing of a theory which was above anything else an act of faith. In fact, in 1912, there was a narrow escape: Carl von Hesse demonstrated in a masterful study that bees are totally color-blind.

Sprengel's daydreams, his hymn to nature, were definitely buried. Happily (and this adverb is not out of place here, for there are some truths which are more emotional than others), a few years later, von Frisch reopened the whole question.

Von Hesse had been guilty of a methodological error, too long and too involved to be gone into here . . . Bees proved perfectly capable of seeing colors, and a whole string of naturalists were to confirm this in succeeding years.

Sprengel had been right intuitively.

care of this job as best they could. It was only at the beginning of
the tertiary that the supreme pollinating insects, the first bees, put
in their appearance.

The pollinating role of insects is of interest not only to the
naturalist or the philosopher, but also to the agronomist. The
major part of fruit and cereal production depends on insects, and
it is estimated that the increase in value of agricultural yield due to
the domestic bee amounts to some ten to fifteen times the value of
its honey and wax production.

All countries with agronomical research services have allocated
funds to the study of these questions which, due to the excessive use
of insecticides, have become most important.

⟨ T H E   S E X   O F   F L O W E R S

The sexual biology of flowers shows amazing variety. Male and
female flowers are to be found both on the same plane and on different plants; there are also hermaphrodite flowers; these may in
certain cases fertilize themselves, either with good results or on the
contrary giving birth to inferior specimens. But in a great many cases
the pollen has to be carried from one flower to the other, and this
transfer is made by insects 90 per cent of the time.

These facts have been known for a long time. The Assyrians
already knew how to lend a hand to nature. By shaking the inflo-
rescence of a date palm's male flowers over female flowers, they
were able to get harvests which they could never have had under
natural conditions.

This was not what Sprengel discovered, but rather the existence
of ways of attracting the insects' attention to the most interesting
parts of the flowers, the nectaries, or nectar glands. Sometimes there
is a series of dots, sometimes converging lines, or again highly-
colored spots in sharp contrast to the general hue of the flower.

In still other flowers, there is none of this—and the phenomenon
cannot at all be considered absolute. These "honey signals," however, have given rise to extended studies, especially in the Germanic
and Anglo-Saxon countries. A most curious discovery has been made
in recent years. Many flowers which had not been thought to be
"signaling flowers," when photogaphed in ultraviolet close-up revealed
remarkable signaling systems.

Naturally, such research has not been carried out haphazardly. On the contrary, it has been approached with the idea of trying to see how the pollinating insect sees the flower.

Of course, it is very difficult for us to find adequate terms to describe these phenomena. We are obliged to accept the use of human terms to describe animal behavior, but when we get to talking of the manifestations of plant life we realize how faulty and misleading the words may be. This very feeling of discomfort is ample evidence of our deep ignorance of those things which are so totally alien to us or, on the contrary, though near to us, totally unsuspected.

⚹ WHAT THE HUMAN EYE DOES NOT SEE

We have been able to establish just how and what bees can see. A team of German and Austrian researchers devoted years to this question. We know specifically that the bee is blind to red, that it has astigmatism, is nearsighted, and sees ultraviolet as the complementary color to green. The flowers' ultraviolet signals are consequently perceived by the collector bee though we are unable to see them. Therefore it is possible to assert that flowers were made with insects in mind and not men.

Less than ten years ago, Mannimes, a young British naturalist, published his studies on honey markings and the behavior of bumblebees. He had studied colonies of bumblebees placed in huge cages containing a wide variety of synthetic flowers. Only the essential elements of the flower were retained, without attempt at likeness. This allowed him to dissect the basic characteristics of flowers, or, more precisely, those which appeared basic in the eyes of the bumblebee.

Among other observations, he noted that when confronted with a disk of a solid color the insects had a tendency to land on its rim. This would be far from the nectar and the pollen, if we assumed it to be a real flower. On the other hand, when the disk had markings analogous to the honey guides, converging lines or series of little dots, the bumblebee would go unhesitatingly toward the center of the artificial flower.

Alongside this optical signal system, we also know of the existence of a whole set of aromatic spots, of which we, of course, can count only those which our own sense of smell can detect.

Some narcissuses have two separate perfumes, the overall odor, and the one emanating from the colored spot which serves as an indicator.

There are flowers which do not have distinctive markings. But there are fewer than were imagined a few years ago when it was not understood that markings might exist in the ultraviolet range. The behavior of bees visiting such flowers is curious: they always seem to ponder awhile before being able to locate the nectaries.

Some of these flowers have very attractive odors and are in great favor with bees. This is so with the magnolia flower. Yet, in its country of origin, America, the principal pollinizers of this plant are not bees but coleoptera, such as beetles and weevils.

STRANGE LOVERS

The properties of certain orchids are much more startling still. Let us take for example the ophrys orchid, fertilization of which as usual depends on insects. These plants have no nectaries, therefore no nectar as bait to attract visitors. They must therefore "choose," if that term can be applied to plants, some other method of attraction. This explains why the ophrys flowers display their "charms" to create sexual excitement in the males of certain species of hymenoptera. The latter then act toward the flower just as if it were a female of their own species, and it is by way of this illegitimate intercourse that the transfer of the pollen is carried out.

The various kinds of orchids do not all attract the same insects, and the methods of attraction exhibit a wide variety of forms. At any rate, stimulation involves several senses: smell, sight, and touch. The ophrys flowers emit aromas very close to the odors secreted by the glands of female hymenoptera. Each species can attract a species of hymenoptera, and usually only that one, but in some cases the plants give off more polyvalent perfumes. These plants thus considerably augment their chances of being "visited" and by the same token their reproduction potential. The chemical composition of the orchids' perfume is still totally unknown to us, as is the makeup of the substances emitted by female hymenoptera.

Visual stimulation also plays an important role; even to the least trained human eye the ophrys flowers suggest the look of large insects.

Many of these facts have been known for some time, but they have been confirmed only within the last few years by a Swedish naturalist, Dr. Kullenberg, who especially brought out the role of the tactile stimuli. The ophrys flower has smooth parts and hairy parts, developed to greater or lesser extents, which in their design reproduce quite precisely the characteristics of female hymenoptera's backs. It is equally remarkable to note that the flower's temperature can be as much as 15 degrees higher than that of the surrounding air. This heat is an additional attractive factor to the insect.

Finally, things happen in this manner: the male hymenoptera, out seeking food, accidentally come near the flowers and are strongly attracted by the odor of the females of their species, an odor which they "know" by instinct. The flowers which in their form and color are so strangely reminiscent of a hymenopter are easy to spot.[2] The insect lands on one of them and, guided by the hairiness of the flower which recreates shapes already imprinted within his nervous system, he attempts to copulate. In the course of this effort, the pollinia, which contain the orchid's pollen, become attached to his body, and, on his next stop, pollinization will take place.

That continues for several days, until the time when the female hymenoptera are born. Then the males abandon their plant loves and with equal passion seek out their legitimate mates.

The procedures used by flowers to attract insects are sometimes lacking in poetry. Sometimes they emit putrid odors which are not without interest to specialists in the uses to which decaying organic matter can be put.

The giant arum of Sumatra, whose flowers grow taller than a man, emits a smell of rotting meat, nauseous to the human sense of smell, but which attracts many carrion coleoptera. Recent research

---

[2] Some such plants bloom only at night. In the huge desert which covers part of the Mexican state of Sonora as well as part of Arizona, there is a cactus with a magnificent flower which comes out during spring nights. This queen-of-the-night cannot be missed, for its aroma can be detected 100 feet away and one plant may carry up to forty opened blooms.

The reason for this all-out assault is that the pollinizers must be attracted, and how else can it be done in the darkness when brilliant colors and seductive forms are useless?

In this case, the target is millers, which must be attracted at any cost, for the flower, which blooms in the evening, will be dead by daybreak, sterile for all eternity, if the moth has not come to her, just as on the contrary she will be heavy with the promise of fruition if her aroma has overcome the distance.

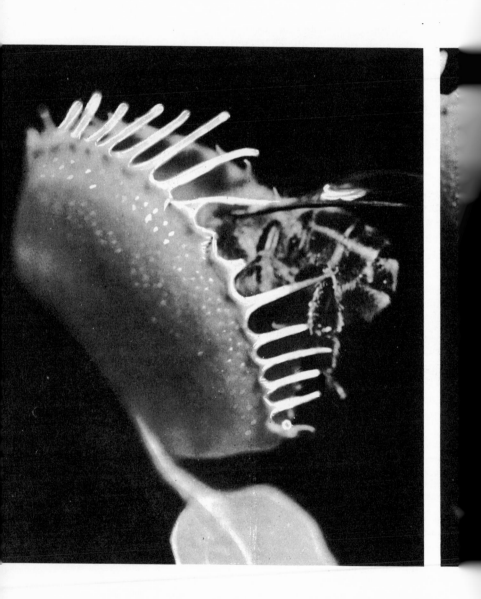

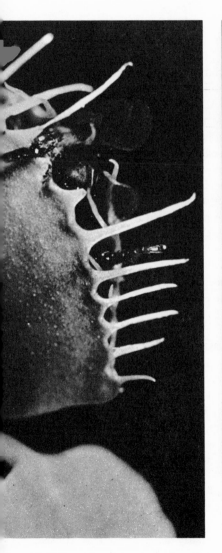
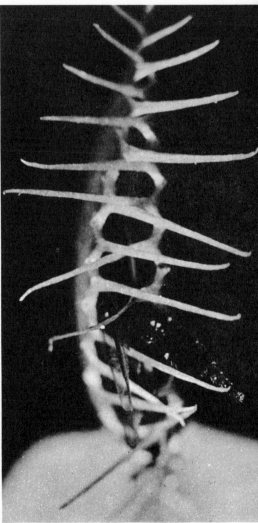

Certain plants use their charms to attract insects which they then digest slowly.—Photos Jack Le Cuziat

has proved that these arums which give off the smell of putrefaction are not in the least wasting their charms. The odor comes into evidence only in the late afternoon, very precisely at the time when the carrion insects are most active in their search for food or new hatching grounds.

✦ DIABOLICAL TRAPS

Another group of plants which have always fascinated the imagination are the flesh-eating plants, one of the elements of the shock arsenal of science fiction writers. According to them, the marshes of the planet Venus contain monsters of this type, endowed with intelligent reactions. However, novelists and illustrators have almost always made the same mistake. Usually, they credit the flower with being a prehensile organ, and they always show the victim disappearing into an agglomeration of tentacular petals.

If these plants eat meat, it is not without reason. The 450 known species of this type are found in the most varied terrains, but always in places where there is a marked lack of phosphates and nitrates in the soil.

Under such conditions, there can be only one solution: to eat beings rich in these vital substances. In order to eat, hunting is necessary, and the plant can count only on its own traps to catch its prey.

Toward this end, there are three types of trap leaves.

First, the simple glue trap; then the replica of a bear trap, in which two jaws snap shut on the victim; and, finally, the pit into which the insect falls without chance of escape.

With all of these plants, a great debauch of means is used to attract the victim, usually an insect, but sometimes a larger animal.

One plant with a glue-type trap, the "sun dew," grows in the shape of pearls, which are shiny and very attractive. Insects are lured to them, get stuck in the glue, and then the redoubtable leaves surround the victim and digest it.

Spring traps are also made up of modified leaves, but they have a fairly close resemblance to flowers and many insects are fooled by them.

The pit type seems to be particularly dangerous. This consists of a cone filled a quarter or a third of the way up with a transparent

Now that we are learning about the psychology of animals, what are we going to discover about plant psychology?

A carnivorous plant devouring an insect.—Atlas-photo

liquid which is a sugary secretion. The cone grows in such a way as to cause the insect to fall into the liquid, which has a lethal effect. It contains "soakers" which make swimming in it almost impossible, as well as digestive juices which carry out a slow dissolving job. The enzymes of these plants are very powerful, but, as they are greatly diluted, their action is slow and the death throes of the insect caught in this diabolical pit of perdition can be very extended.

At the end of the last century, an Anglo-Saxon author almost succeeded in convincing the world of the existence in Madagascar of a giant carnivorous plant capable of swallowing a human being. He had even dreamed up a horror novel built around worship of the plant with, of course, the sacrifice of a virgin to it at certain periods. The whole thing was a pipe dream. There is no carnivorous plant of such size on our planet. The largest is a plant of the "wolf pit" or snapdragon type, whose cone reaches the quite impressive depth of one foot. This allows it to trap some small mammals as well as birds attracted by what appears to be a perfectly inoffensive watering trough, but not men.

Let us point out that the flowers of these carnivorous plants are completely inoffensive. How could it be otherwise? Flowers are reproductive organs, not nutritive organs. They are temporary organs, short-lived and fragile. The traps of these carnivorous plants are not flowers at all, but are simply modified leaves.

⚐ TOWARD A LABORATORY OF PLANT PSYCHOLOGY

In the examples which we have just cited, the plants get the maximum out of the insect. In the case of pollinization, the flower makes repayment for the service rendered. It offers its pollen and its nectar, or even its charms,[3] as in the case of the ophrys. From

---

[3] There seem to be certain olfactory affinities between the tastes of man and those of the insect.

Apart from the odors intended for the carrion-eaters, day- or night-blooming flowers generally delight our sense of smell.

And that is a happy coincidence, for, if the insects did not have the same tastes as we—well, don't forget that flowers were made for them and not for us.

But let us consider as an example a tree which, in order to assure its pollinization, attracts strange animals: bats. This tree grows in the eastern part of Africa; it is known as the sausage tree because its fruit looks very

the flesh-eating plants, on the other hand, the insects stand to get only death in return. Nevertheless, in one case as in the other, the seduction or attraction procedures are the same. It all takes place as if the plant knew what would attract the insect.

We have long since given up refusing to believe in the intuitive knowledge of animals. That a chick might run to cover on seeing the outline of what looked like a bird of prey seemed to us unbelievable for a long time, and it took many years and many experiments to convince us that this could be so.

Now we face another enigma: the possibility of analogous traits within the vegetable kingdom. Will we some day create plant psychology laboratories in order to familiarize ourselves with this "inhuman world"—this world which becomes more fascinating every day, as we begin to admit that in it there may be forms of thought and will which are radically different from our own?

---

much like large brown sausages. Its flowers are of a very dull color and their aroma, it seems, has a strange similarity to that of a litter of white mice. While the smell that greets us in laboratory mice pens may not be particularly attractive to our nostrils, it is ideal for those of bats.

So we can consider ourselves fortunate to have the same tastes as the honeybee or the bumblebee!

Beyond Society

BEYOND, or alongside, social phenomena, there are a great many facts which are difficult to classify. For those interested in societal phenomena, ants have some advantages over bees, and to a lesser extent over termites: a great variety of forms and conditions of life and a more developed evolution in certain areas. In particular, they bring together integrally within the life of the colony a large number of individuals often widely separated from each other in the sphere of zoological classification.

The communications set up between neighboring ant hills show that these societies are not as exclusive as those of bees. Facts which have been known for a very long time strangely reinforce this assertion: the existence of slavery, domestication, and social parasitism.

It may seem paradoxical to consider slavery as a proof of the evolution of a society. However, in this zoopsychologists agree with sociologists. A society which takes no prisoners is undoubtedly much less highly developed than those which keep slaves, however badly the latter may be treated. The height of intolerance is to refuse even to allow another being to exist. I do not know whether such an attitude does exist within human societies in its absolute state. It is to be found among honeybees, and many science fiction authors have dramatized the similarities between civilizations of this sort and the human world.

The first discoveries of slavery in ant societies date back to the time when we were just learning about colonies in which two different groups cohabited in more or less temporary association and about the raids carried out by warlike tribes. As early as 1810, Huber was studying these phenomena, and he had already understood that these were "slave traders'" forays.

One of the best known of the ant slavers is the red ant or *formica sanguinea*. This insect is to be found in the north of Asia, in Europe, and America. Periodically, armies of workers take to the warpath and attack the nests of the equally common black species, the *formica fusca*. They kidnap the larvae and pupae of their vanquished enemy and carry them off to their own nest, where they are for the most part brought up with the greatest care. The adults born of this nest of eggs will spend their entire lives within the new colony, but the name of slave seems hardly suitable to them. Indeed, the *fusca* workers in the ant hill will lead quite exactly the same lives as do their "masters," doing the same work and enjoying the same privileges. The exact significance of this strange behavior did not appear to us until about 1905, when Wheeler discovered that it had its roots in the habits of the young queen.

The queen of the *sanguinea* is not able to found a new colony by herself. After having been fertilized during the nuptial flight, she has to locate a hospitable nest. So she selects a nest of *fusca,* takes possession of a few larvae, and kills the workers who try to take them back. The workers born of this nesting immediately assume a submissive attitude toward the queen and help her raise her own progeny, who in turn retain the kidnaping instinct and from time to time go out in a group to capture nests of eggs from neighboring colonies. Yet this slave system does not seem to be especially profitable to the kidnapers; it is in no way indispensable to them, and in some colonies the pillaging trend seems to be disappearing.

It is not quite the same, however, with the amazon ants. The workers of this genus, to be found in the same regions of the globe as the *formica sanguinea,* are equipped with very special mandibles: remarkable weapons that can be used for nothing but massacring opponents, not for digging the earth, not for seizing most prey, nor even for feeding the young. These two razor-sharp sickles force the ants to become warriors and to practice slavery. The strategy and tactics of the amazons have often been described, and always admiringly.

The *fusca* workers, which here again are cast as the victims, generally do not try to resist. If they so much as suggest the slightest shadow of defense, the amazons snap their mandibles shut and slice their heads off.

The founding of a new amazon colony by a young queen is carried out in a manner reminiscent of that of the *formica sanguinea*. The queen breaks into a small colony, kills its queen, and subjugates its workers. These workers, along with the others captured on later pillaging forays, accept the domination of their kidnapers. They dig the earth to make the ant hill, hunt the prey, and feed the larvae. They never follow the warriors out on their expeditions, but captivity changes their character rather strangely: the *fuscas,* usually so timid and peaceful, become aggressive in the image of their masters. But the masters in their turn are also influenced by the slaves.

Sometimes the latter are not taken among the *fuscas* but from another species. According to Forel, in cases when the slaves belong to the *rufibarbis* species, the amazons' expeditions begin to take place at different hours, their columns are set in a tighter formation, and they go off at greater speed. We can hardly keep from making

The ant's antenna is a masterpiece of miniaturization.

—Photo Holmès-Lebel

comparisons with the numerous examples in human history of conquerors undergoing changes through the influence of the subject peoples.

Sometimes it appears that the situation reverses itself completely: it happens that a slave species accompanies its masters on their pillaging forays and carries off the nests of eggs of their own species. Wheeler goes so far as to write that "in this case, the slaves are really the masters, and they seem to use the latter only to dismay or frighten the colonies whose eggs they wish to steal." This interpretation seems daring, to say the least. However, we must admit that it is difficult to give any other which is perfectly satisfactory.

To say, as Picard wrote some ten years later, "Nothing in parasitism or the slavery system is especially mysterious or complicated, none of it, at any rate, is outside the ordinary customs of ants," is not very convincing either. How, in spite of differences in shape, color, size, and odor, can these ants coexist with each other? How do the masters know that the lives of slaves within their cities must be respected, while the very same species will be massacred during the next foray? Let us be allowed at least to contend that all this is, on the contrary, rather complex and somewhat "outside" what might in general be anticipated in an insect.

It was Huber who discovered slavery among ants. Here is how he himself described his coming across a swarm of ants leaving on a raid:

"On June 17, 1804," he wrote, "walking in the outskirts of Geneva between four and five in the afternoon, I noticed at my feet a legion of rather large red or reddish ants cross the path. They were moving rapidly in a body; their troop covered an area about eight to ten feet long and about three or four inches wide. In a few minutes, they had all completely left the path. They went through a rather thick hedge and entered a field, into which I followed them; they snaked across the grass without getting lost, and their column remained continuous in spite of the obstacles that they had to overcome.

"They soon arrived near a hill of ash-black ants, the dome of which arose in the grass some twenty paces from the hedge. A few ants of this species were at the door of their abode. As soon as they saw the approaching army, they attacked the leaders of the horde;

the alarm was spread at the same moment within the ant hill, and
their companions came swarming out of all the underground passages. The reddish ants, whose main body was only a couple of
paces away, rushed toward the foot of the ant hill; the whole troop
assaulted it at once, turning back the ash-blacks, who, after a very
brief fight, retired to the depths of their home. The reddish ants
climbed the heights of the hillock, grouped themselves at its summit
and thronged into its first pathways; other groups of these insects
were meanwhile digging with their teeth to make themselves lateral
entrances into the ant hill; this undertaking was successful and the
balance of the army poured through the breach into the besieged
city. They did not stay there very long; three or four minutes later,
the reddish ants came back out through the same openings, each
carrying in his mouth a larva or a nymph of the invaded ant hill."

Oldtime authors were very severe in their condemnation of slave-
holding ants; Sir John Lubbock used the following terms to pillory
a species of ant which seemed especially decadent by the standards
of Victorian morals:

"*Polyergus rufescens* gives us a striking example of the decadence
brought about by slavery, these ants having fallen into complete
dependence on their slaves. Even their anatomical structure has
become considerably altered; their mandibles have lost their teeth
and turned into simple pincers, certainly lethal weapons but useful
only for war. They have lost most of their instincts: their art, which
is to say the builder instinct; their domestic habits, for they pay
no attention whatever to their young who are entirely turned over
to the slaves; their industry, as they take no part in gathering the
daily food supply; if the colony moves its ant hill, the masters must
all be carried to their new home on the backs of the slaves; worse
than that, they have even forgotten how to feed themselves."

↑ PASTORAL CIVILIZATIONS

Aphids or plant lice are the domestic animals of ants. A meeting
between an aphid and an ant usually brings about the following
scene: the ant approaches the rear end of the insect which will be
its "cow." Using its antennae very adeptly, it tickles the aphid. The
latter, in response, emits a small drop of sweet liquid. This liquid
is immediately absorbed by the ant, which seems to take great

pleasure in it and repeats the performance until his crop is chock full. Usually, two or three drops are enough for this; but there is one exception: among the American ants of the *myrmecocystus* genus, some of the workers act as honeydew reservoirs. That is to say, the ordinary workers bring them the sugary secretion of the aphids in such quantities that their abdomens become distended and grow grotesquely huge. These living vats suspend themselves from the ceiling of the ant hill and dispense their supply as needed to those who know how to trigger them with a special poke of the antenna.

We might wonder how the ant became accustomed to "milking" the plant louse and by what kind of process the carnivorous species learn to respect the lives of succulent prey so as to get an even greater benefit from them. That an insect should know enough not to kill the goose that lays the golden eggs is something for us to think about.

If some ants are satisfied to come in contact with aphids accidentally, others, to varying degrees, have learned how to domesticate them. Among certain species like the *lasius,* the aphid eggs are kept in the ant hill all winter long by the ants, who take very good care of them. When spring arrives, as they hatch out, the lice are then carried onto the kind of plants they like. From then on, they are very regularly milked. In exchange, the ant swarm delegates guards who watch over them day and night, not only to forbid any attempt at escape, but also to protect them energetically in case of any attack whatsoever against the aphids.

Some ants are even more careful and bring their stock back into the ant hill every night, at least as long as the nights remain cold. In these subterranean stables, the "cattle" are corraled near edible roots, and when these seem used up the aphids are moved to another spot. Other species protect the herd by building temporary shelters outside.

Despite this perfected husbandry, the *lasius* remain interested in accidental finds, and, while some of the workers stay home at their "cowherd" jobs, others go through the woods looking for "wild" plant lice.

One science fiction writer wrote a short story involving a group of humans captured by another intelligent race. The humans, shipwrecked on a desert planet, do not look like much and are immedi-

The immense, little-known world of the ants holds many surprises.
An ant lying in wait for a louse.—Photo Rapho

ately put into a terrarium in the zoo of the capital city. They try to make their intelligence felt through various means, but in vain—until the day one of them catches a sort of mouse and puts it into an improvised cage. A few hours later, the doors of their enclosure are opened, and the humans are given back their liberty, with profuse apologies. For, the outer space specialists say, only an intelligent being is able to deprive another creature of its freedom.

No doubt this author was unaware of the psyche of ants. But such a story well illustrates the fact that we spontaneously give great value to such behavior.

It is also most interesting to go back to some other observations which still remain open to discussion. For example, it has been reported that ants carry winged and sexed aphids—which appear at the end of the summer—to the tops of trees so as to facilitate their nuptial flights. So perfect an adaptation, if it were verified, would certainly necessitate explanations less simplistic than the kind usually given.

Many other animals maintain relations with ants. More than 3,000 such species have been counted. The most interesting are those which are sought out and kept by ants. Aphids are far from being the only domestic animals around the ant hill. There are many others, some of which are very strange.

Certain caterpillars have glands which secrete a sweet liquid which ants prize. When a worker comes across one of these "vending machines," which has only to be tickled in order to operate, it knows better than to harm it in any way. The caterpillar is carried back to the ant hill at the cost of strenuous efforts, and the whole colony is allowed to take advantage of its offerings. When we say the whole colony, we have to watch what we say, for the caterpillar during this time is eating up the ant larvae! In spite of this, the caterpillar is kept there for months, until the day when, turning into a butterfly, it has nothing more to offer and, knowing better than to expect gratitude from its hosts, it loses no time in flying away.

The adaptation, in this case, seems highly developed and, if the ant can get along without the caterpillar, the opposite is not true. Several authors, indeed, insist that if it is not periodically licked and palpated by ants, the caterpillar will die of infection in the glands secreting the sugary liquid.

Rather frequently, termites of different species also live in association and tolerate each other perfectly. Grassé noted one very complex termitary on the Ivory Coast built jointly by five different species. Some species even seem to show a penchant for the neighborhood of alien termitaries. Sometimes two populations live next to each other, while at other times they mix completely. Yet the nature of these relations and their importance to the insects are still a complete mystery to us.

The termitaries of tropical countries shelter a flock of insects belonging to very diverse species. The relations between termites and their guests no doubt reveal as many variations as among ants, but we have only the slightest amount of information about them. As a general rule, the biology of the animals of tropical regions, where naturalists are less numerous and have been working for a shorter time, without doubt still holds many surprises for us.

INTOXICATION, DECLINE, AND SUICIDE

There is stranger still: the case of the coleoptera called the rove beetle. The rove beetle is a carnivore which avidly devours the ant larvae. It does not lay eggs but live larvae which it deposits within the nest of ant eggs. The worker ants, far from getting rid of these intruders, on the contrary take great care of them and even deprive their own progeny of food for their benefit. The ants seem quite unaware that much of the attention they give to these larvae is harmful to them, for only the neglected and forgotten larvae develop into adults.

It is fortunate for the ants that this is so, for the presence of a given number of these parasites can quickly bring about the demise of the colony. Here is how it happens: the workers, as we said, feed these larvae at the expense of their own brood. In exchange, the larvae give them a sort of exudation which the nurses seem to relish. When the rove beetles grow up, they force the worker ants to feed them. It seems that they are perfectly familiar with the system of communication, a tapping of the antennae, which the ants use among themselves to request food. In this, they are well ahead of us, for while we may be aware that there is such a code, we have not yet found the key to it.

But all of this is as nothing against what the rove beetles offer the ants in return. The hairs of their abdomen secrete a liquor which produces stupefying effects on the ants. The workers, who seem overly addicted to this substance, literally become intoxicated with it and fall into a state of drunkenness or profound stupor. During this time, the work is, of course, not being done, and the poorly-cared-for queens give birth to bastard individuals, intermediate between queens and workers, unable to accomplish the jobs of the one or the other. These workers who look like queens are perpetually on the go, running this way and that futilely, and quickly bringing about the downfall of a colony in which they represent too great a proportion.

Wasmann, studying these phenomena more than forty years ago, spoke about them as "social vices," and used this subject as the matter of veritable philosophic debates. According to him, the associates of the ants, like those of the termites, are the result of a "friendly selection," comparable to our own deliberate choice of our domestic animals.

If this line of reasoning has generally been rejected, the fact no less remains that the problem of social parasitism persists. It becomes even more complicated when we try to connect it with mimetism. Certain inhabitants of ant hills look strikingly like workers even though they are not. A single example will be enough to prove its complexity: the most complete case of mimetism to have been recorded is that between the coleoptera and certain nomadic ants, known as dorylines or army ants. The workers among the dorylines are almost all blind and yet, without being able to see, take on the appearance of the other insect!

It will be a long time before we are in possession of enough facts to explain such phenomena.

✓

The Secrets of Orientation

✓

A few years ago, the pigeon-fancying world was completely puzzled to learn of events which seemed unbelievable and yet had happened on several occasions during international speed and distance meets: out of several hundred pigeons starting the race, only a very few reached their goal. Was something happening to the presumably infallible instinct of the homing pigeon? [1] Naturally, the breeders did not think so, and they blamed the upset on radar. The radar waves, they said, were disturbing the birds' sense of direction, and they were therefore responsible for the strange failures of the recent competitions.

At the same time, zoopsychologists were taking a renewed interest in the problem of migratory animals and their return to the nest. In Great Britain and Germany efforts to understand how birds navigate were made by the observation of captive birds; everywhere in the world, more and more detailed migration maps were being drawn up.

Bird migrations have essentially been studied through the method of ringing. A Dane, Mortensen, carried out the first scientific ringing on starlings in 1890. Since then, a great many ringing and recovery stations have been established around the world.

The percentage of recoveries varies greatly according to the species. It is naturally much higher for game birds. On the average, it is 16 per cent for wild ducks as against only one per cent for warblers.

[1] A homing pigeon in championship races accomplishes quite remarkable performances. It is not rare for a champion to go a distance of 400 to 500 miles at a speed of about 28 miles per hour.

Let us therefore try to sort out what has been discovered and separate certainty from speculation. The work of a British researcher, Matthews, can be taken as our point of departure.

⌁ PERFORMANCE

First of all, a question: what are the limits to this well-known sense of direction?

It would seem that birds have immense potential in this regard, and the world's record no doubt belongs to a seabird, the puffin. The puffin was brought to Boston from its native isle located off Wales, and was found back home twelve days later, having taken only ten hours longer for the trip than the letter which told of its take-off. This voyage home represented a distance of over 3,000 miles, and of course all birds are not capable of doing as much in so short a time.

Outside of artificial homing experiments there are the annual adventures known as bird migrations, which require a sense of direction up to any test. For instance, there is a sea swallow, living at the northernmost end of Canada, which spends the winter at the edge of the Antarctic Continent, covering a matter of some 12,000 miles twice each year. And the world's record for migration, observed on a ringed bird, is held by a seabird which was marked in Great Britain and turned up in Australia.

To explain such truly astonishing feats, the most varied theories have been put forth. One of the earliest contended that birds are able to locate the magnetic pole, through an inborn compass, or that they could follow so-called "great electromagnetic streams." These hypotheses, we should point out without delay, are invalidated by a very simple experiment: if a magnet is attached to the foot or neck of a pigeon, the percentage of returns to the nest is in no way modified.

A second hypothesis had recourse to what are known as the forces of Coriolis, produced by the earth's rotation. These forces were named for the French mathematician Gaspard de Coriolis who, in the first half of the nineteenth cenutry, described the forces of inertia.

He demonstrated that the laws governing the movement of bodies could be applied in a rotation system if one included in the equation

An ordinary sight but a source of extraordinary enigmas: a flock of migrating birds.

Swallows over Dublin.—Photo Penelope Reed

a force of inertia, operating toward the right of the direction of motion if the system is rotating counterclockwise, or toward the left in the opposite case.

It at first seems impossible that a bird could perceive the infinitesimal variations of this force, but certain drifts observed in some migrations might be explained by the effect of these forces which undoubtedly do drive masses of air from the north toward the southwest. Unfortunately, the forces of Coriolis can have an effect only upon bodies in flight above the surface of the globe; yet it has been experimentally established that this tendency to fly from northeast to southwest already existed in caged birds. Before starting their flight, such birds turned themselves on foot in the right direction.

It would be wearisome to enumerate all the more or less fantastic hypotheses which have been brought forward to try to explain these orientation phenomena. Therefore, we will limit ourselves to the ones which seem the most plausible.

Radar is capable of recording bird migrations. This is not without danger, for it may be feared that, in some especially hot period of the so-called cold war, one of the antagonists might mistake a flight of wild geese for missiles and respond in kind.

The first bird migration recorded by radar in Great Britain did bring about a general alarm. It happened on a November night in 1941. The radar stations located on the Norfolk coast reported the approach of a veritable armada of enemy ships, accompanied by strong air cover flying at very low altitude. Air-raid sirens sounded, ships put out to sea, and fighter planes took to the air. But the blips on the screen became stranger and stranger, and it was soon discovered to everyone's satisfaction that all that was involved was a flight of wild geese heading for their usual grazing grounds at the mouth of the Humber.

However, we can overlook these drawbacks when we realize the fascinating results obtained by ornithologists utilizing radar. It was in this way that we were able to discover a series of high-altitude migrations, taking place at some 16,000 feet or more, which heretofore had escaped detection. In the same way, the extent of nocturnal migrations turned out to be a great surprise to observers.

An English specialist has recently drawn up a summary of the results thus obtained, all of which seem to demonstrate the existence of an orientation mechanism not unlike those used for human navigation.

Among his remarks, there are some curious ones. Flying over oceans, birds follow a straight line, which does not deviate when they go from day to night or vice versa. They do not drift laterally. On the other hand, they become disoriented when the sun or the stars are blacked out. At night, birds do not seem to follow the coastline; during the day, they appear to do so or not, at will. This would mean that, like men, they have two navigational methods: astronomical and visual. Finally, a violent wind can bring about serious upsets, sometimes involving a complete change of direction.

As Matthews points out so correctly, it is quite strange that man should have navigated for centuries by depending on solar coordinates and that we should still have been so slow in realizing that birds might operate in exactly the same way. And yet, for the bird as for man, the most highly developed sense organ is quite obviously the eye.

⟨ SOLAR NAVIGATION?

Here then, is the hypothesis which, at the present time, seems the most logical. The element essential to orientation is the solar arc, or in other words the visible trajectory of the sun. The plane enclosing this arc forms an angle with the horizontal. It is the measurement of this angle, constant for any given spot, which allows us to determine its latitude. From north to south, this angle grows larger and larger, and if the pigeon knows the arc of his cote, he can find his way north or south, according to the arc he observes in any unknown location.

In the same way, observation of the trajectory of the sun, or of a fraction of that trajectory, allows one easily, provided he is familiar with the solar arc of the site, to know whether he is east or west of it. Since the height of the sun depends on the time of day, we must also admit that the bird is provided with some sort of internal "clock." That would not be surprising in itself, and birds are not the only animals to show such capabilities; bees, for example, do have such a "clock," the existence of which has been well-established for a long time. Recent experiments have further confirmed this assertion; it is possible to accustom bees to come out of their hive only once every hour by making food available to them at a set time. Once this rhythm is acquired it persists for a long time, whatever the external circumstances may be, even including moving the hive from Europe to America, as has been recently tried.

It has further been demonstrated that a bird's visual sharpness, thought less extreme than man's, allows it to measure very small angles and that, beyond this, the bird's perception of motion is more developed than man's.

Additionally, motion picture films taken at very high speed have made it clear that a bird's head remains perfectly horizontal at all times during flight, even when its body is not. A compensating mechanism allows the muscles to maintain this position through information relayed by the inner ear, the stabilizing organ. In this way, they achieve the equivalent of an artificial horizon such as the one used by aviators who, unlike sailors, do not have the surface of the sea for an aiming-point. For all these reasons, it seems logical to admit the hypothesis of solar navigation. But—for there is always a "but"—there are nevertheless a number of points which remain enigmas.

⁊ NOCTURNAL MIGRATIONS

How do the equally numerous nocturnally migrating birds find their way?

For this, too, hypotheses are not lacking; some specialists say they use the moon, others the stars.

Recently, in a planetarium, a German studied the possibility of warblers guiding themselves by way of the constellations. The first results seem to prove that they do.

Can this mechanism break down? Is radar capable of confusing such extraordinary navigators as pigeons? Five writers have tried to prove that radar affected birds, while two others were unable to establish any reaction whatsoever, despite carefully performed experiments. On the other hand, we do know that certain kinds of radar can create auditory reactions in human beings nearby; we also know that some radar stations have been attacked by bees. In every in-

Thousands of wings and one goal: biologists and the military would like to know the mechanisms involved.

Terns in flight—Photo Mauritanie

stance, these effects have occurred only at very short distances, and it seems foolhardy to assert that the homing of pigeons might be seriously affected by radar.

⌁ SOME STRANGE DISCOVERIES ABOUT MIGRATION

A Berlin ornithologist, Oscar Heinroth, tried a very curious experiment with migratory birds. He knew that British wild ducks are partially sedentary and that those which migrate go very far south by way of Spain. Finnish ducks of the same species all migrate, but take a different route. Heinroth took some British duck eggs to Finland and had them hatched by Finnish ducks. These ducklings, at the end of the summer, followed the route of their foster parents and the next year came back to Finland. There is therefore no innate knowledge of the migration paths, which are either determined by external factors or learned through example.

The second hypothesis, however, is undermined by the fact that the ducklings of British origin did not start their migration till a month after their foster parents, at the time when British ducks, less anxious to leave a comparatively temperate country, usually take to the air.

Among the strangest of migrations, we should mention that of the Tahitian cuckoo. This bird travels to New Zealand to lay its eggs in others' nests and then flies off, over the oceans, to look for islands in the area extending from the Carolines to the Tuamotus. However, it avoids the large land masses such as New Guinea and the Australian continent.

Some birds also migrate by swimming; this is the case of penguins, which cannot fly. It appears that some species travel as far as 650 miles or more and come back to the very same shore to raise their young.

But birds are not the only animals able to return to a starting-point or to hold to one direction without deviation.

✦ THE SECRET OF THE SALMON

Fish give us many examples of similar behavior.

The story of eel migrations is well-known; less lengthy migrations of herring and sardines have also been recorded. The salmon is a particularly striking case since it is able to find its way to its native river after spending several years at sea. This return trip to the river of its youth is made for the purpose of giving birth to a new generation of salmon.

The migrations of red tuna are also impressive. In the mouths of fish that have been caught, fishhooks originating in the Azores have been found, to the fisherman's surprise, in Sardinia, Turkish hooks in Algeria, hooks from Brittany in the Mediterranean, Spanish ones in Norway, and so on.

Fish migrations are an even more puzzling problem than those of birds, no doubt because man, who is "visual" more than anything else, is better able to understand the behavior of a bird which after all can see landscape beneath it unfolding like a map. When we realize that astronomical navigation is involved, bird voyages seem much less disconcerting to us than those of an animal whose vision is sharply reduced by its aquatic surroundings.

The only way to determine whether salmon really return to their native rivers is by marking a maximum number of young fish. The number of fish marked has to be extremely high, for it is generally believed that only four to five per cent succeed in coming back to the reproduction sites.

The first attempt to mark fish is supposed to have taken place in 1653 in a river in Great Britain. But the first scientifically controlled experiment did not take place until 1905. The fish were marked by the insertion of a silver wire in the spinal fin. Later these fish were found back in the river from which they had started; the first came back in 1906, the last in 1909. Many similar experiments, made both in Europe and in America, further confirmed what had been sensed until then.

For a long time, a theory due particularly to the oceanographer Le Danois explained the salmon's return to the native river in a very simple way. He claimed that all salmon caught by trawlers on the high seas are found in areas which can be demonstrated to cover former riverbeds now under the ocean. It is known that the English Channel is the former riverbed of the Seine now under water, the Irish Sea that of the Mersey, and so on, and the traces of these submerged valleys can be clearly found. The salmon therefore had no trouble in getting back to his native river, since in fact he had never really left it.

This theory is a good example of the repugnance shown by the human mind to admitting a fact which is apparently inexplicable in the current state of scientific knowledge. Apart from its being quite improbable that one can correctly distinguish subterranean valleys and its being difficult to see why the salmon would go back up the Seine rather than the Thames, an examination of fishermen's hauls shows us that many salmon are caught outside of the submerged valleys.

At any rate, salmon marked in the river and then recovered at sea give us irrefutable proof that the salmon has a real memory for places. It is enough to cite one result obtained in France by Vibert, an engineer of the Waterways and Forests Service.

In the Oloron torrent, he marked about 8,000 young salmon at a spot some 30 miles up from the sea. Of this considerable number of marked salmon, six were recovered at sea, all off the coast of Brittany. These recoveries having taken place after markings made in different years, it seems to be proved that young salmon of the Oloron torrent finish their growth on the shoals off the Finistère.

Here are average lengths and speeds of the voyages: 469 miles at 17 miles per day, 406 miles at 18 miles per day, 406 miles at 17½ miles per day, 419 miles at 14 miles per day, 375 miles at 16 miles per day, and 356 miles at 16 miles per day. In this estimate of speed and distances covered, it is assumed that the young salmon moves in an absolutely straight line, which is by no means certain. At any rate, one must be struck by the constancy of the results which, it must be remembered, were spaced over three years. The theory of the submerged valleys therefore does not hold up.

Many other hypotheses have, of course, been advanced to explain how the salmon finds his way. Some asserted that physical and chemical peculiarities of the water play an essential role, especially, the oxygen or carbon dioxide content, or the degree of salt concentration. Others believe that the olfactory apparatus of the salmon is able to detect very slight differences in odor and that this fish gets back to his river through his sense of smell. Naturally, those of opposite opinions asked this question: if rivers have characteristic odors, do not these odors vary from one year to the next? Moreover, is there not a greater difference between the odor of a river at its source—which is where the salmon is born—and that at its mouth, than there may be between two different rivers?

These questions remain unanswered; but to the question of whether a fish can distinguish between two different waters and can carry a lasting recollection of them, we can readily reply in the affirmative.

AMERICAN TESTS

Under laboratory conditions, it has been possible to teach not a salmon, but a minnow, to select one particular water, and that recollection is retained for a long time, especially if inculcated at the beginning of the fish's life. Experiments have also shown that it it possible to condition salmon a short time after their birth by pouring into the river very small quantities of any given chemical substance. Later on, the adult fish will assemble wherever that substance is in evidence. These experiments suggested to American researchers a rather interesting series of tests, the purpose of which was to study not just the return to the native river, but the return to a given arm of that river. This return was found to be so precise that, if the waterway splits in two, the salmon coming to the fork will always select the stream in which they were born.

A group of salmon were caught as they were going up two tributaries to the Issaquah River in the state of Washington. They were marked with different colors according to the place of their origin and released downstream of the confluence. Half of these fish were released as is, the other half with their nasal cavities stuffed with cotton. The normal salmon without exception went back to their original stream; those without smell, on the other hand, swam around haphazardly. The planners of this experiment felt fully satisfied, though one can easily surmise that loss of the sense of smell might upset the general behavior of the fish and that the test therefore does not constitute absolute proof.

Fishes' sensitivity to the temperature of the water and an awareness of the contours of the riverbanks through the organs of the lateral line have also been considered.

THE SUN? THE STARS?

The imagination of researchers, as can be seen, has proved boundless. And yet it has not gone far enough, for, according to the latest information, in the case of fish as well as that of birds, it is necessary to introduce the element of celestial navigation. Salmon, whose vision is far from being their sharpest sense, are nevertheless quite capable of perceiving the position of the sun when they are not swimming at too great a depth. In fact, they do better than that, according to a German zoologist, Braemer, who has studied these questions both in his own country and in the United States.

His principal experiment takes place in a circular aquarium of no great depth, mounted on a pivot, which is placed in the shallow water of a lake, but rather far away from the shore, in such a way that the fish in the aquarium cannot see any reference point. The fish is then put into the aquarium, and he has a choice of sixteen exits through which he can get, if not to free-flowing waters, at least to a spot which he might consider a safe shelter. Fifteen of these exits, arranged in a circle, are obstructed, and the fish must learn to find the one open door correctly. Observations are made through a periscope which is moved continually so that it cannot be used as a reference point either, and, during the apprenticeship period, the whole aquarium turns several degrees at each new test.

Finally, in another series of experiments, the test set-up is placed in a dark room in which there is a thousand-watt bulb, acting as a "sun." Not only has this proved the fish's capability of recognizing the cardinal points of the compass, but it has also proved his ability to follow the movement of the sun. One example can illuminate this.

After the fish has become habituated to finding, at midnight in the dark room, the exit in the direction of the artificial sun, he will, during the day, at high noon, head due north. North is the midnight direction of the sun, and this all would seem to point to the fact that the animal is completely aware of the apparent direction of rotation of the sun, of the point in space at which it must be at a given hour, and also necessarily of what time it is.

𝗒 THE LIVING CLOCK

This knowledge, incidentally, is different according to whether the fish is a native of the southern or northern hemisphere, the visible movement of the sun which determines south or north at noon being in opposite directions in the two cases. Is this, then, an innate mechanism or an acquired one? So far, we do not know. But we know much more about bees, which also have their ways of telling time and the course of the sun. The domestic bee is quite as adept at this as the fish or the bird, and we have more or less convincing evidence that this also holds true for many other animals.

As for determining the visible movement of the sun, a bee native to the northern hemisphere should be thoroughly confused in the southern hemisphere. A study made in Brazil gave evidence that, while recently imported swarms showed many signs of confusion, those which have been in the country for some time appear quite well adjusted. Kaimus, who discovered this interesting phenomenon, has suggested the hypothesis of a mutation which has taken place within the last three centuries since the importation of bees by the conquistadores. The truth, however, seems to lie elsewhere; it would appear that the bee is capable by its own means of making the correction: 500 flights outside the hive appear sufficient to allow for adjustment to the hemispheric change. There is still to be explained how the young honey-gatherers are advised of this change and how they are taught by their elders to follow the visible movement of the sun.

That an insect should be able to master something so complex might appear surprising, and yet the red ant of the woods has the same abilities.

At the beginning of the spring, the workers among them are not able to follow the movement of the sun, while at the end of the summer this presents no difficulty to them whatsoever; this has just been established by the German, Jander.

Fish, then, particularly salmon, guide themselves by the sun, and they are perfectly able to find their bearings in any season and under any latitude. The bee and the ant have the same ability and use similar procedures for finding their way home after having explored the neighborhood; but are there other animals capable of doing this?

Mammals have been very sparingly studied on this score. While we may know something about the great historical migrations of American bison or caribou or certain African antelopes, these animals have become rare too quickly to make them the subjects of thorough studies. Among rodents and even domestic animals, such as the cat or dog, we can find amazing stories of their making their way home, but in fact it seems to be more difficult to do studies of these animals than of the great migrators.

↗ BEYOND DEATH

Another example of rather extraordinary migration is that of a butterfly, the North American danaid or monarch butterfly. Each year at the same time this insect disappears from the northern United States to go south and lay its eggs. It faithfully reappears in the north the next year. But it is not the butterflies that make the southward trip that return north. After the eggs are laid, one generation dies out, and it is the next one which returns to the territories inhabited by its parents. What is most truly strange about this story is that each year the insects choose exactly the same stopping-off places for their rest en route so that there are what might be called butterfly trees, which in appearance seem no different from their neighbors. Before the conquest of the continent, Indian tribes worshiped these trees with superstitious veneration, and American entomologists have sought in vain to find physical or chemical difference between these trees and the others.

↗ EMIGRATION

Beside migrations proper, which involve departure and return, it may be worthwhile to note that there are also emigrations.

The emigrating insects, sometimes erroneously referred to as migrators, are well-known, in particular grasshoppers, whose "flights" sometimes reach the proportions of thirty miles wide, involving trillions of individual bugs.

But now let us go on to a controversial area which some consider forbidden territory although others, with some justification, would like to include it within the domain of the rational.

There are quite a number of unusual stories of animals' navigational abilities. Although it is not possible to effect all the verifications required to make these stories acceptable without reservation, they are certainly not without interest.

There is, for instance, the greyhound César who followed his master from Switzerland to the court of Henry III in Paris; he got there only three days after the coach in which his master had traveled.

One dog, during World War I, did even better. This animal, named Prince, somehow or other crossed the English Channel and one day turned up in the trenches alongside his master.

Since 1950, the laboratory of parapsychology at Duke University, in North Carolina, has been studying instances of "return home" of domestic animals: 500 quite extraordinary cases have thus been recorded and have been analyzed in a critical study.

The cases of unusual behavior break down into four overall categories: 1. those which suggest that the animal has some foreknowledge of a danger threatening him or his master; 2. those which seem to foretell the unexpected return home of the master; 3. the animal's return home; 4. "psi-trailing." This last category, which has been considered in a particularly interesting study by J. B. Rhine and Sara Feather, covers the cases of animals which, separated from their master or an animal companion, follow him under conditions which seem beyond the capabilities of their actual senses.

The Duke laboratory workers after a first analysis decided to consider only 54 cases of psi-trailing, 28 of them involving dogs, 22 cats, and 4 birds. These 54 cases were then severely scrutinized. The first elimination factor is the absence of specific identifying marks. People may say that their cat or their dog, having covered thousands of miles, has found his way to them. But there is nothing to prove that it is indeed their pet. At any rate, the belief of the persons involved, however well-founded it may be, cannot be accepted as scientific proof. This fact accounted for the elimination of four cases.

A second elimination factor is the distance covered by the animal. Often enough, this is too small to be considered decisive, and the performance may be explained by random wandering and the spotting of a scent or some other recognizable element. Arbitrarily, a minimum of 28 miles was set, and 29 cases were thus eliminated.

Another reason for elimination: the time lapsed since the event. If only one witness is left, the case becomes difficult to document and, on this basis, 4 other cases were dropped.

One other reason, which has nothing to do with scientific validity, was uncooperativeness of witnesses. For fear of publicity, or for other reasons, some people to whom the investigators had been referred refused to give any specific details.

Fifth element: cases in which the identifying signs seemed definite, but were of a psychological rather than a morphological nature. A dog named King allegedly traveled all the way from Idaho to California to be with his master. On arrival, the dog was emaciated from the three-month journey, but he definitely had the same habits as King. He always raised his left forepaw to shake hands, took up his sleeping position on a certain sofa, jumped into the back seat of the car and put one paw on the driver's shoulder, and so on. But such behavior, to tell the truth, is common to many dogs, and it is not enough to be considered convincing, so three more were ruled out.

When these are all added up, we see there are not many probative cases left. Among these, there is the story of Smoky, a Persian cat identifiable by a small tuft of red hair under the chin, a rather unusual characteristic. The M. family, who lived in Oklahoma, moved to Tennessee. Some 19 miles away from the Oklahoma home, Smoky got lost during a roadside stop. Two weeks later, neighbors saw him prowling around the Oklahoma homestead for several days. And a year later, Smoky appeared at the new Tennessee house, having traveled approximately 300 miles.

Another case which is not open to question is that of Sugar, also a Persian cat, who would not get into the car which was taking his family from California to Oklahoma, almost 1500 miles away. Sugar was adopted by neighbors, but after 16 days he disappeared. Fourteen months later, Mrs. W., Sugar's mistress, was looking out the window one day when a cat jumped up on her shoulder. At first Mr. W. thought she was joking when she said that Sugar was back, but he had to accept it: the newly arrived cat had exactly the same callus on the hip and showed every other resemblance to the cat they had left behind, on the other side of the desert and the Rockies.

There was also Tony, a dog who wore an identifying collar. Tony was a black dog, of no discernible breed. His masters moved from Illinois to a town in Michigan, some 225 miles away. Left in the care of friends, Tony caught up with his masters in a matter of six weeks.

But the most extraordinary case of all is probably that of pigeon 167. His owner, young P., who was only twelve years old when this adventure took place, had raised this pigeon with tender care. One day, young P. became ill and was taken to the hospital 65 miles away from his home. The tame pigeon, of course, was left at home by the child's parents. A week later, on a dark and snowy night, the boy called the nurse and told her he could hear the rustle of wings outside the window. To keep him happy, the nurse opened the window, and a pigeon flew in. The boy, who could scarcely believe it was true, recognized his pet; he told the nurse so, and asked her to read the number on the band around his leg. The nurse picked up the pigeon and, to her amazement, read off exactly the number the boy had said would be there. This particular story has been carefully verified; it took place in 1940, and it was the subject of a radio broadcast, at which the various witnesses confirmed it to the last detail.

Owners of pets would be hard put to understand why there should be such doubts about their ability to recognize unerringly a cat or dog who had been with them for several years. They know very well that it is easy to recognize an animal you have loved and that there is little likelihood of making a mistake. But Rhine and his co-worker no doubt had good reasons to be wary of that part of the scientific world which would be unwilling without incontrovertible proof to believe in such extraordinary happenings. Rhine concluded his work by laying out the general lines for a systematic study of the subject.

✓ TELEPATHY?

The most interesting animal for such suggested study, without doubt, is the pigeon, and it should be possible, by taking advantage of one of these birds' attachment to a human being or one of its own kind, to create a repeatable experiment, which would of course be one of the indispensable conditions of the study. Attachment to one of its species could of course be a sufficient motivator; there is another story which proves this to us.

A family was traveling one day from Redondo Beach to San Francisco, over 450 miles away. With the family were two tame pigeons and their young. The birds, raised at Redondo Beach, had never made the trip before. Halfway there, they stopped for a picnic, and the male pigeon flew away. They called after him, they waited, but he was gone. On arrival in San Francisco, the cage with the female and the little ones was hung up at a window. Next morning, there was the male on the window sill. The cage was opened, and he hopped right in.

It should not be believed that the exploits of domestic pets setting out to rejoin their masters are as difficult to check up on as some people contend. Here are two cases which recently took place in France.

First, there is the story of a cat named Mastic, who with his brother, Pinceau, lived with the family of Ligier, a plasterer, at Buxières-les-Mines, in the Allier. One day the Ligier family moved to Sainte-Geneviève-des-Bois, in the department of Seine-et-Oise, about 165 miles away. Pinceau was perfectly happy with the change, but Mastic disappeared after two days. Neighbors of the old Ligier home were amazed later on to see Mastic reappear. He had gone back over the whole distance, crossing a number of rivers, including the Loire, in a matter of nine days.

The other story is about a dog. Boby belonged to a florist at La Ferté-Alais. He was two and one-half years old when he went with his master to the flower market in Paris and there got lost. He had been to Paris only twice before. Since his master was unable to find him despite all his efforts, the master and his children finally had to return home, convinced the dog was lost for good. Yet, five days later, exhausted and caked with mud, Boby turned up back home.

It was not the distance—about 35 miles—which was amazing, but the fact that this country dog, unaccustomed to the big city, had found his way through the maze of Paris streets and the roads of the surrounding suburbs.

It may be felt that I have gone into too great detail on these stories while often I have had to pass briefly over other authenticated discoveries, but it is just the fact that they are so far off the beaten path which justified the detailed telling of such events.

Let us remember the care with which these typical stories were selected and not be afraid to question them. What other theory, besides telepathy, could explain such phenomena? Nowhere in the arsenal of known facts can we find an explanation that covers them.

How, then, are such affinities between man and animal formed?

It may well be true that certain races are more prone to this than others. Persian cats turn up repeatedly in the examples that have been cited, without however there being anything exclusive about it.

In most cases it will also be noted that there was a child in the family. Perhaps the affinities between children and animals are different from those which can occur between animals and adults. The love of a little girl for her cat, or the attachment between a boy and his pigeon—these may well be the subject of a study which will bring glory to some dignified scientist of tomorrow.

CHAPTER VIII

The Wonders of Apprenticeship

IN 1960, the American government decided to declassify the strange research of Professor Skinner. This made it possible to make his work public.

Professor Skinner is indeed a picturesque character. Among his claims to fame are his having taught a pigeon to play the piano and rats to play marbles. Nevertheless, he is not in charge of a carnival sideshow but is a professor of psychology at the University of Indiana.

The research he carried out during the war had been kept on the top-security classified list, for it had investigated the possibility of having a pigeon act as a guide for a missile.

The pigeon's eye is known to be a highly perfected mechanism, and a bird brain (popular usage notwithstanding) turns out to be a real brainteaser—even for a builder of electronic machines. To be able to put such mechanisms to work guiding a missile seemed a most exciting idea.

A pigeon can learn a great many things. In particular, it can learn very quickly to aim its beak at one particular picture, mixed in among a number of other more or less similar pictures, and to go straight for the heart of the picture. During the training period, for each "goal" it scores the pigeon receives a grain of wheat or other reward; once the apprenticeship is completed, the bird is fully conditioned and hits the target or targets pointed out to him without letup.

Nothing easier then than to train a pigeon to aim at a given point of an aerial photograph or on the outline of a warship. Thereafter, the pilot bird is put into a missile, where he is shown on the screen a picture of the terrain, thanks to an optical arrangement or to radar.

When the target to be hit appears, the pigeon pecks at it, and if he pecks too high or too low a correcting mechanism immediately changes the missile's course. Only when the peck hits the exact center of the screen does no correction need to be made, and then the explosive heads for its objective.

Skinner had even conceived of the idea of using several pilots, and some of his missiles had as many as seven pigeons in them. Under those circumstances, if one pigeon had made a mistake, majority rule would have carried the day.

It is also possible to train pigeons to follow complicated itineraries. A rather complex training thus allowed an air-to-earth missile, launched from a high-altitude plane, to reach a shore 20 miles away, at which point the pigeons directed it toward a port located approximately five miles away, and then, being above the port, they steered toward a warship somewhat over a mile further on and, getting into close range, finally selected one smokestack as their specific target.

Skinner got the idea of what might be taught to pigeons in 1940, but it was not until 1944 that he was able to get the birds ready for action. At that juncture, American scientific war research was entirely concentrated on the atomic bomb, and Skinner's demonstrations did not get the hearing they deserved.

Now that his research has been made public knowledge, we know this is not the only way animals can be used in wartime. The Russians have proved that: dogs which had been trained to retrieve their food from underneath tanks were released with an explosive load attached to them and headed under German armor. They were able to cripple attacks which no other means had been able to stop.

In the light of what we know of the sensory potential of birds and other animals, we can rightly ask whether, within the purview of modern warfare, such overwhelming weapons should be dismissed as negligible.

According to Professor Rensch, there are considerable differences in the apprenticeship possibilities of animals of even closely related species where their sizes vary greatly.

Little animals are always immediately far ahead of larger ones where easy problems are concerned. If the problems are difficult, the large animals always seem to win out finally, with the little ones showing more and more "nervousness" and "shyness." Relative size is the only significant factor on this count. Thus, fish of the family of cyprinodontidae (or microciprini), which are considered "giants" of their kind though they are only about two and a half inches long, act in relation to smaller ones like giant chickens in relation to chickens of dwarf species.

Memory also seems to be much greater in proportion to the larger size.

An animal, as we have already seen, is quite capable of perceiving many things that our most intricate instruments have trouble apprehending, and it is also able to learn a great many things.

In reality, any living being, even an amoeba, is capable of being taught, but, to tell the truth, the performances of single-cell organisms are not exactly spectacular. A paramecium can be taught to swim in a triangular pattern or in a square; all that is required is to keep it confined for a time in a container of such a shape, and then to set it loose in a larger circular aquarium. It is a minor result, but it does demonstrate the ability of even the lowest of organisms to acquire habits.

One level above, we find the starfish.

The bed-of-nails experiment was conceived around 1885 by Preyer. You immobilize a starfish on a board by driving a nail, as close to the body as possible, between each of its five arms.

Escaping is rather difficult for the starfish; it can do so only by learning to use its arms in other than its habitual way as it has to make each arm autonomous in order to get out of the trap. As the experiment is repeated, the starfish gets out more and more rapidly. After 70 tries, the time it takes decreases from seven minutes to three and one-half. Which shows that the starfish, too, is able to learn.

The earthworm can learn to find its way through a simple maze. This is a T-shaped tube, one branch of the top of which has a dark shelter which the worm likes; the other, by contrast, is plainly distasteful. If it goes in there, either it comes in contact with sandpaper, which it cannot stand, or else two wires give it an electric shock, which it also dislikes.

At the beginning the worm moves at random; but soon, one can detect a hesitation in its behavior, and it turns back the other way before it gets to the end of the branch which holds the disagreeable surprise. Finally, after a very large number of tries, usually more than 150, it makes no more mistakes and invariably turns in the right direction.

It is interesting to note that if, at this time, the two branches are inverted, it will take the worm only one or two understandable mistakes to reroute itself correctly. The earthworm, then, has not only been able to learn, but even, within limits, to generalize. Yet, it has only the simplest kind of nervous system and its brain is hardly worth mentioning. If the experimenter cuts off its head and the first five rings of its body, that makes no change in what it has learned. It is, therefore, the whole of the nervous system which has acquired the education imparted by experience.

This possibility of retaining acquired knowledge in one part of the body has recently led to some very strange experiments. Some young researchers at Michigan State University studied the birth of conditioned reflexes in flatworms, the relatively common turbellarians.

 ⸱ A S C H O O L F O R F L A T W O R M S

These worms have unusual regenerative properties. If they are cut in half, each half grows into a whole again within a matter of about four weeks. The idea of trying to find out what might be retained of conditioning after such an operation was of course an appealing one; Connel, Jacobson, and Kimble carried this job out successfully by using a relatively simple technique.

Some fifteen worms were placed in a small aquarium over which hung an electric light and which was equipped to give its occupants an electric shock. The light went on two seconds before the electric charge came, and very quickly the worms started to react characteristically to the shock from the time the light went on. This, of course, is a very common conditioning. What came next was less so. Using scissors, the experimenters cut each worm in half and put the severed heads and tails into separate aquariums.

The experimenters found that all of the regenerated worms, both those building from an original tail and those from an original head, retained the memory of this training. Specifically, where it had taken an average of 134 tests for the original whole worms to learn the reflex, the worms reconstituted from a head got their "knowledge" back after only 40 trials and those starting from a tail after 43.

Such a difference signifies nothing, and we can therefore affirm confidently that it was the whole of the nervous system which retained the memory of the conditioning. Yet, the original acquisition of the conditioning itself cannot take place if there is no head, and a decapitated flatworm is not able to learn anything.

With mollusks, we find ourselves making a major step forward. Some members of this group have achieved a very high degree of evolutionary development. The cephalopods (octopuses, squids, and such) are almost the equal of vertebrates in the matter of psychic development.

Not the least telling aspect of the study of the animal psyche is the realization that some groups have in this regard gone to the limit of their potential.

Mollusks, in particular, have reached a very advanced stage. Boycott, for one, trained octopuses to move through a fairly complicated maze. Other experiments led Piéron to conclude that, on the mental level, the octopus is superior to many vertebrates: fish, batrachians, and reptiles.

The insect world also opens perspectives in this area.

⌁ A SCHOOL FOR ROACHES

All insects are capable of learning, and even the lower insects are able to master the difficulties of relatively complex mazes.

Rémy Chauvin, for instance, spent many years studying the behavior of the small German roach. His maze was made up of metal blocks about an inch wide and almost three inches long. These blocks, laid end to end, allow the construction of almost any maze, from the simplest to the most complicated. The whole of the course is painted white and very brightly lighted. The metal blocks are in a shallow tub holding water, so that the maze is surrounded by water on all sides.

The roach, placed carefully at one end of the maze, is not at all comfortable. It "hates" to be this way, in unknown territory, under a bright light; what it likes is dark shadows and protective crevices. It therefore sets out to find a more comfortable place, and being unable to get out of the maze and having no relish for a possible bath, it finally finds the desired shelter, at the other end. This shelter, a darkened glass tube retaining the scent of other roaches who have inhabited it, most certainly represents a haven to the insect, which now absolutely refuses to leave it. The experimenter, nevertheless, takes hold of his victim delicately, puts it back at the starting point, and repeats this procedure ten times. The animal is given a three-minute rest between each two trips, and, at the end of the tenth run, it is allowed to spend a half hour in its shelter. Then the experiment starts again, with another ten trials. Naturally, during the whole course of the operation, the experimenter notes carefully how long it took the roach to negotiate the trip to the shelter as well as the number of errors committed, that is, the number of turns into impasses.

Comparison of results obtained during the first set of ten trials with those of the second set is spectacular. For the insect has absolutely learned to make not a single mistake by the time the second set starts.

What is extraordinary is that the method of getting to know a maze is scarcely different for a roach than for a rat. Phenomena which seemed to be amazing when discovered in mammals reappear in almost identical form in insects. Latent training is a good example of this. If an animal is simply put into a maze and left there, without anything which constitutes either a trap or a reward, it takes very readily to this new environment and wanders about it haphazardly. If after a given time the animal is taken out of this maze and placed in another identical one, but one which has a trap and a reward, in no time at all the subject learns to negotiate the maze without any error whatever in such a way as to avoid the trap and get the reward.

This discovery, made in the thirties, created quite a sensation. Tolman felt that it was necessary to allow for the existence of what he called a "cognitive map" within the brain of the rat, and the fact seemed quite unbelievable. Yet, nowadays, we know that the same thing exists in roaches, and the matter seems much less surprising to us.

The attitude of psychologists who evinced surprise at the existence of such a possibility strikes us as particularly naïve, and it requires some explaining.

Zoopsychology was able to come into existence as an experimental science only by an extraordinary feat of stripping down. As long as it was essentially made up of anecdote and assimilation to man, it seemed a mere copy of the physical sciences.

For a long time, only minor details seemed worthy of note, as if one were trying to study the atoms and molecules that made up psychic action. We were a little like art critics trying to write a general history of painting and studying only children's drawings, while disregarding Michelangelo and Rubens, on the theory that one must start from the simplest and progress toward the more complicated if one is to carry out a scientific study in the prescribed manner.

The error was not in studying the reflex or the tropism, but in coming to the conclusion that an animal had no notions beyond these. For it is absolutely obvious that an animal must know the area in which he lives; that is necessary so that he can get back home, to his food, and many other things, and it is really not surprising that he should be acquainted with the topography of the neighborhood. Whether insect or mammal, this is certainly a vital necessity to him.

As far as the higher insects, such as bees and ants, are concerned, they take care of themselves very well in a maze, but such experiments as these have not brought out in them any capability which could clearly be interpreted as a superiority, despite the fact that they are certainly much more evolved than the roaches.

⟋ INSIGHT

On the other hand, observation of the behavior of insects has allowed us to believe that some of them at least must have insight. By insight is meant a higher form of training or apprenticeship. Instead of there being a slow but constant reduction of the percentage of mistakes they make, we usually note a sudden sharp decrease in this figure, with no later relapse. The subject has understood, through his insight, and for him then the problem simply no longer exists.

The faculty of learning was long held to be a sign of intelligence, and it was maintained that it could not exist in invertebrates. Yet, Thorpe, as a result of the study of quite a number of publications, showed that there were most certainly types of apprehension through insight among insects. The bee in this way suddenly has knowledge of the location of its hive; builder-wasps react correctly and without hesitation to the destruction of a part of their combs; the ammophila or sphex learns with lightning speed to be aware of the landscape around his home range.

Among lower vertebrates, fish have given rise to interesting studies. They find their way quite well through rather complex mazes. We can speak of insight where they are concerned, but also of a faculty of "preadaptation," noted by Herter. The potential of certain fish would appear to be far beyond the actions they are called on to carry out during their lives, and if they are confronted with an unusual problem for which they have a preadaptation, they will show a quick positive response, which one cannot necessarily attribute to insight.

Herter thus cites the case of a fish which normally becomes active only at twilight. Nevertheless, this fish distinguishes very well shapes and colors he never has occasion to use and reacts to these stimuli which would have appeared to us as being foreign to his psyche.

One especially interesting aspect of apprenticeship among fish is the effect of example. A shoal of fish learns the complexities of a maze more quickly than does one isolated individual.

Let us not concern ourselves with amphibians or reptiles, which have thus far been the subject of very few experiments.

We saw at the beginning of this chapter how highly developed was the potential of birds for apprenticeship. Latent ability for training and insight are common with them, and often they in no way lag behind mammals in this. However, we should linger awhile over the most highly developed forms of apprenticeship among the latter.

It is very difficult to draw any overall impression of the research done in the last 25 years in the area of training. There are no less than 7,000 published references relating to white rats in mazes, but we know of very few attempts to synthesize conclusions.

The work performed by the American school of animal psychology on the behavior of rats in mazes did permit the formulation of a large number of laws which apply generally, yet it was somewhat lacking in enterprise. The rat is an especially gifted animal, and it can certainly do much better than merely find its way without error through a maze, even a complicated one.

Let us skim quickly over some of these laws. The first is the "law of motivation": if the reward is particularly tempting, the rate of learning goes up. The second is the "law of the gradient of the goal": the animal tends always to get closer to his goal, and he will correct his direction if an obstacle temporarily turns him away from it. Then there is the "law of latent apprenticeship," of which we have already spoken, and the "law of anticipation," characterized by the animal's tendency to try too quickly to make the requisite directional changes. Finally, the "law of insight" completes the list, which can be left at that.

The most spectacular cases of training have, however, not always been carried out with scientific aims. Circus animals and their trainers' art are worthy of lengthy study. This was very well understood by Professor Hediger, currently head of the Zurich Zoo.

After having consulted with the most famous of animal trainers, he himself opened a training station and, after several years of work, was able to translate into scientific terms the intuitive lore accumulated from generation to generation of tamers. Hediger brought out the strange assimilations which a captive animal makes between his native *milieu* and the one imposed on him by man. In this way, the cage assumes the value of a territory, and within this cage certain spots become privileged points, shelters, dungeons, such as we have mentioned earlier. The stool which is always found in a tiger's cage is a good example of one of these key spots within the territory.

Another important notion is that of "flight distance." All animals in their natural state have the habit of not allowing a possible enemy to get closer than a certain limit. If the adversary comes beyond that limit, the animal may find it prudent to flee, but when flight is absolutely impossible, there is only one solution: face up to the enemy and fight.

In the artificial living conditions of the circus, these limits are considerably reduced. The wild animal trainer, without ever having put these laws into words, is well aware of them. As he comes closer, he knows that the beast will retreat, but he also knows that if he continues, the animal will get on the defensive in a most spectacular manner. If he really knows his job, he will be able to work fantastic effects, ferocious roars and threatening gestures, without any great risk, for there is always a limit between the distance which provokes only a bluff and the one that triggers a real fight.

Finally, we have already spoken of the phenomenon of domination in animals living in bands. Among many vertebrates, the social unit is the "harem." Among wild horses, zebras, vicunas, and otaries, the male constitutes a permanent harem including not only his females but a few young. The males have most ferocious fights with each other in the course of trying to steal the females.

This phenomenon of domination is of use with certain circus

animals, such as lions, and the tamer can take advantage of it to gain an actual hold on his beasts. If he can become integrated into the group and be accepted as number one, the game is won and training becomes extremely easy. The technique is relatively simple and has been known for a long time: the tamer must walk about the territory, be the first one in the cage, and therefore take on the prestige of the "first occupant": he must also assume a dominating, even provocative, attitude, which, though expressed in the body of a human, is readily "understood" by the animals.

After that, the trainer has to establish language conventions between himself and the animals. To let tigers know that everything is fine, a tamer will normally use a "prrr," which to these animals is the sound of extreme satisfaction. On the other hand, the lion tamer, under the same circumstances, will utter an "oo, ah, ah," which to them means the same thing. Other purely artificial signals will then be added to this vocabulary.

When a man has achieved this degree of familiarity, almost any kind of training becomes possible. That is how spectators get to see dolphins playing basketball or gorillas riding bicycles.

ᛏ WHAT CAN BE GOTTEN FROM A CHEESE

Let us, however, come back to the laboratory experiments, for some of them also are most spectacular.

An American of Asiatic extraction, Tsai, carried his experiments with rats very far. He used as attraction a piece of cheese.

In one of the experiments, the rat must first climb a ladder to a platform; there he must pull a swing toward him with a string, jump into the swing when it comes within his reach, and take advantage of its motion to carry him over to another platform where he can get the cheese.

In another experiment, the only way the rat can get to the platform on which the cheese is is by pushing, for quite a distance, a cart on to which he must then climb to reach his goal.

All of this, it would seem, is only child's play to the rat, which will learn anything the experimenter wants it to, provided there is a piece of cheese as a payoff.

A particularly amusing experiment was carried out in an American laboratory. Within a cage there is set up a food-distributing machine based on a very simple principle: each time the rat presses on a lever, a ball of food comes out of a nearby opening. Once the animal has been trained to this, a slight change is effected. The lever is put at one end of the cage while the food distribution now takes place at the other end. The rat quickly gets used to this minor switch.

Then, three rats are put into the cage, all of whom have had the same training. The situation becomes particularly tense: the rat who works the lever never gets anything as a reward, for the other two who are watching make off with the food before he can get to it.

During the first day, none of the rats wanted to press the lever, and all three waited desperately in front of the opening, from which of course no food came at all.

The second day, one of the rats pressed the lever, but only to the advantage of his companions. On the fourth day, one of the animals had a stroke of genius: he quickly pressed the lever three times in a row and, while each of his fellows grabbed one of the balls, he was able to eat the third one at his leisure. Then, he went back to work, and within two hours he had released no less than 1,156 food balls, which allowed all three to glut themselves. His companions of course found his good efforts most acceptable: one of them, during all this time, did press the lever three times, but the other did not even deign to touch it.

For a certain time, the scientific world thought it had proof of the possibility of transmission from one generation to the next of data acquired through apprenticeship.

A researcher named McDougall had chosen the white rat as the subject of his experiments and put him through a rather painful test. He wrote of the results in several publications which attracted a lot of attention in the thirties.

The animal was dropped into a tub filled with water and having two outlets, one lighted, the other dark. The lighted outlet was equipped with a most distasteful electric-shock apparatus, while the other led to a more agreeable spot from which the rat could get back to his cage.

The rats were subjected to this involuntary bath repeatedly until they learned to avoid the electrified exit each time. McDougall, studying the progress of 32 successive generations, noted happily that the rats learned faster and faster with each new generation and that the inheritance of characteristics acquired through training was thus established as an experimental reality.

But, at the same time, four researchers at an Australian university, surprised and interested by McDougall's first results, tried to verify them. At first they found remarkable progress from one generation to the next. Going beyond McDougall's limits, they followed 41 generations with the same kind of positive results. But at this point the results obtained by the rats became less good, decreased in quality for five generations, and then picked up again through the 51st and final generation studied.

The key to the enigma was to be found in the control which McDougall had failed to carry out. Checkup rats, raised in the same room, were also tested from time to time by the Australians. Despite the fact that their ancestors had undergone no training, the results shown by these rats displayed broadly the same fluctuations as those of the animals descended from the trained strains.

It would then seem, or at least this is the hypothesis currently accepted, that the breeding of rats is subject to slow fluctuations in their general state of health. More or less lasting microbial infections or certain deficiencies may occur and have a considerable effect on the rat's psychic powers. What McDougall and the others had been studying was the fluctuations of the general health of the rats they bred and nothing else. We have to admit this is rather disappointing, but it is better to understand the truth about McDougall's experiment, which is still sometimes cited as proof positive of the inheritance of acquired characteristics. And yet, we must stress that one negative experiment does not in any way prove that such heredity does not exist.

A SCHOOL FOR APES

If we look into the apes, we will find even more amazing things. One Yale Laboratory researcher used the food-distribution principle to carry out studies which have become classics.

During the first stage of the experiment, the ape was given a certain number of white chips which, put into a machine, would each cause the release of a grape. Then, once the apes had understood the value of the chips, these were given to them only as a reward for work done. Dr. Wolfe, who was in charge of the experiment, would give chips only to those who had raised a 20-pound weight to a certain height. The apes went diligently to work, so diligently in fact that some of them collapsed from exhaustion; one of them had actually lifted the weight 185 times in ten minutes.

After that, in addition to white chips, blue chips were used which were worth two grapes each. Once the chimpanzees had learned to value the blue chips at twice the white, Wolfe started to use yellow ones, which were good for one ride on the shoulders of the experimenter. Then still other colors were added, each one representing a different value.

One day, a rat having come into the cage, one of the chimpanzees, who was terrified of these rodents, ran to his chip collection, took out a yellow one and came back and offered it to Wolfe, who, deeply touched by this, could do nothing but take him up on his shoulders.

ɤ   T H E   R A T   L I K E   T H E   C H I M P A N Z E E

This experiment went on a long time. At some times, the chip distributor did not operate at the same time as the grape distributor, which made it necessary for the apes to save up their wealth.

Finally, and not out of any sadistic aims, Wolfe put the chip machine in one cage and the grape machine in another. Then, the chipless ape locked in with the machine would beg chips from his neighbor, who would give them to him. Unfortunately, this story has no moral, for the beggar never offered to share the goodies thus gotten with the benefactor who gave him the chips.

These experiments attracted a great deal of attention when they were published, but what was more striking was that Tsai, undertaking to repeat them with rats, obtained very similar results. A rat can learn to pull on a rope which will bring down a chip which he then carries to a saucer in which in exchange he will be able to get the piece of cheese he never seems to have enough of.

All of which proves that we probably still have no idea how far the training of the more gifted mammals can be carried, and that the study of the larger simians, most particularly, still holds considerable surprises for us.

CHAPTER IX

ⵏ

The Builder Animals

ⵏ

SINCE it would be impossible to enumerate all the known types of builder animals—which indeed are legion—we will content ourselves with citing a few cases which illustrate their behavior.

Spider webs do not inspire in everyone the disgust which housewives feel when they discover one of these works of art in a corner of the apartment; a web descried of an early morning, shiny with dew, has often been sung by the poets, and the one on a vintage wine bottle provokes nothing but respect.

ⵏ THE SPIDER AS ARCHITECT

For the naturalist, there are two kinds of webs: the trap-web and the home-web, to say nothing of all the intermediaries. The material employed scarcely varies: it is the silk secreted by the animal, coming from glands situated in its abdomen and having openings known as spinnerets. This silk is not very different from the kind produced by silkworms, and sometimes it is of remarkable quality.

We are mainly familiar with the trap-webs, which are more frequent in nature than the others. Everyone knows that the spider lives on the prey caught in these traps. Some of them are rather unesthetic, such as those irregular dirty-gray ones spun by tegenaria in attics, cellars, or even apartments. Such a web is intended exclusively for the capturing of prey, and the spider does not live in it; its home is made up of a simple tube of silk, open at both ends.

Naturally, we prefer regular-shaped webs. Those of the epeirids are often extremely beautiful. These animals, like Penelope, undo

A skilled architect and diabolical assassin, a spider must eat to live.
A spider attacks its prey.—Atlas-photo

their handiwork each night to start it over again; so we can see them at work frequently in the middle of the night. To begin with, the spider must be concerned with the directing thread—the very skeleton of its construction. The spider must drop to the ground after having fastened the thread to the top of one plant and climb up toward another. Then this brace must be pulled taut, and several thicknesses finally give the rope dancer a visibly solid cable. Sometimes the epeirid uses a device which spares it a lot of trouble. It drops one tenuous thread and waits for the wind to hook it on somewhere; after that, it climbs up on this fragile bridge and reinforces it in the usual manner.

After having set this first horizontal thread, the epeirid's work is a routine matter. It attaches a thread to the first one, drops to earth, takes a few steps and then anchors the thread in such a way that it is definitely oblique. It goes back up and sets a new thread which it then attaches diagonally to the second so that it has a triangular frame within which to set the rest of the web. The radii are quickly finished, and on them are set several spiral twists, known as temporary spirals.

When the building of the insect-trap starts, the quality of the material used changes; the silk becomes a sticky thread, coated with mucus. Using this sticky thread, the spider builds the final spiral, woven about twice as tight as the original. This is the general plan, but it allows for many variations. The web is not always so regular; with some species, one or two sections of it will be missing; with others, the center of the spiral does not coincide with the geometrical center of the frame. Sometimes, the webs are not vertical, but definitely on an angle. Finally, it happens that the webs may be decorated with silk ribbons, the exact meaning of which we do not know.

The argiopes, for instance, end their webs with a very decorative zigzag, often referred to as the spider's signature, for its outline varies with the species and allows us to identify them. The size of the webs also varies considerably; among the largest of the regular ones are those of the nephila. These spiders, which live in the tropics, particularly in Madagascar, weave huge webs that go beyond four feet in diameter. Social spiders break this record by building webs that may be seven, eight, or even ten yards long; but it is true that there are a lot of them on the job: thousands of workers may cooperate on these collective works.

✓ THE SPIDER AS ENGINEER

Other webs are worth our consideration, for they are more complicated traps. This is particularly true of the web spun by a spider of the *menneus* genus. This small web is stretched over the animal's outspread legs. If a prey comes in contact with it, the spider lets everything go, and the net closes remorselessly over the unfortunate insect. The habits of this spider still being largely unknown, we cannot yet tell whether it passively awaits its victims or whether it goes hunting after them actively like the retiarii of the Roman arenas.

Another somewhat similar trap is that of the hyptiotes. The web is triangular, with its base anchored solidly while the top is held by the spider by means of a thread. As soon as the prey touches the web, the spider releases the thread, and the victim is caught.

Other traps are also very unusual, such as the one of a certain South African spider which spins only a very rudimentary web and leaves hanging from it a very sticky ball at the end of a silk thread. The spider, sitting up in the web, twists the thread between its legs, making the little ball spin around rapidly. This strange bait, it seems, attracts irresistibly all kinds of small insects, which get themselves stuck on it.

We should mention another very curious fact which naturalists for a long time were unwilling to admit. This is the use of a counterweight—a tiny pebble at the end of a thread—to keep the web taut. The epeirids, which spin the beautiful geometrically perfect webs we have already mentioned, often employ such a method. More recent observations tend to confirm that this is definitely done on purpose and not because of an accident resulting from the retraction of a thread caught on a pebble on the ground. Counterweights of this kind have been found hung more than a yard above the ground, and only a concerted effort by the spider could explain such a stratagem.

There are also the numerous webs which serve both as traps for the prey and homes for the builders. Some of these habitations are

The spider seems to have taken a course in geometry. We know now that certain drugs can cause him to build irregular webs.

—Photo Roger-Viollet

worthy of closer study. Such a one is the diver's bell of the argyronetidae, an aquatic spider, which is certainly a curiosity.

We also know about the edifice constructed by a spider living in southern France. This is a very regular-shaped web, in the center of which there is a silk sac covered with débris of various kinds. This serves not only as a shelter for the spider, but also as an incubator for its young.

But let us stop a moment and observe the strange behavior of a tropical spider, the nephila, which does not destroy its web nightly as do the epeirids and others, but rather gives it maintenance and keeps it in a state of repair. This peculiarity attracted the French zoopsychologist Lecomte to study this repair system, thereby adding a chapter to our knowledge of the spider's psychic abilities.

*   ON THE THRESHOLD OF RATIONAL
    THOUGHT

The nephila's webs are, as mentioned previously, of huge dimensions; they reach more than four feet in width, have a roughly triangular shape, and are spun at a slight angle from the vertical. When a foreign body is placed upon the web, the spider immediately goes toward it but reacts differently according to whether it is prey or something to be rejected. The vibrations of a victim struggling in the trap are certainly one very useful method of information, but the nephila unerringly recognizes a piece of meat or a dead insect, which it either eats or stores away at the top of the web. If, on the other hand, it is some unwanted foreign body, some flake of wood brought by the wind or a leaf put there by the experimenter, the nephila carefully detaches it and throws it wide of the web.

It is especially interesting to see how the spider gets rid of a long piece of sewing thread dropped curlicued on to the web. If the thread is on the lower face of the web, things are relatively simple; the spider gets hold of one end of the thread, which it frees from the sticky silk, and it then follows the thread in all its convolutions, progressively letting it trail off behind it. If the thread has been put on the upper face, it has to be slipped through the web itself, and this later has to be repaired.

The spider handles these problems so well, and they seem so much to be the kind that it frequently encounters, that the experimenter is very much tempted to complicate further the situations it will have to face.

⌄ THE SPIDER UNDERSTANDS MECHANICS

So he drops a new sewing thread on the web, this time having first attached the other end of it to the ceiling of the room in which the experiment is being made. If the thread is placed on the lower face, again there is no difficulty. The spider detaches it from the web and it hangs loose alongside, which does not disturb the spider. But if it is caught on the upper face, the problem is harder to solve. In most cases, the spider simply moves its web. But in some rather rare cases the spider will run one of its silk threads under the foreign thread and in this way raise it away from the web, until it hangs free. This rather surprising behavior allows us to "credit these spiders with an implicit knowledge of certain laws of mechanics."

Another accomplishment reinforces this impression. We have already said that the web is spun at a slight angle to the vertical. Tension threads tauten this web in such a way that the slightest vibration can be felt by the watcher. It is possible to force the spider to spin its web on a frame mounted on a pivot, which puts it in a horizontal position. The spider adapts quite readily to this condition, but since the web thus placed has a tendency to sag and no longer vibrates, the spider here and there attaches suspension threads to it, which it connects to the ceiling, thereby giving back to the trap all of its qualities.

These observations, as well as others made while watching titmice repairing their nests, suggested to Lecomte the formulation of a law.

This author, surprised at the stereotyped nature of the original constructions as against the variable character of the repairs, brought forward the hypothesis that "a statistical study of the variations of behavior of an animal species, in a given situation, would no doubt show an inverse relationship between the frequency of the appearance of the situation and the variability of the responses." The rarer the situation is, in natural circumstances, the greater the variability of the animal's reaction. And by a rare situation, we mean, not one which may occur from time to time in the life of the animal, but a truly unprecedented, artificial circumstance, before which the instinct is not capable of supplying an immediate stereotyped response.

With these considerations, we will be done with spiders, even though we are far from having exhausted the subject; let us rather see now how honeybees build their wax cakes.

⋎ THE HONEYCOMB

Honeycomb building has been studied with great attention in France by Darchen. His method was to confront the bees with a certain number of problems, the solutions to which gave the researcher answers to his own questions.

The workers build the comb out of small flakes secreted by their glands, working in chain fashion as a team. In this way they form a small ellipsoidal ridge which grows rapidly while retaining its general shape, its longer axis always remaining parallel to the direction of gravity. The growth areas are the vulnerable points of the construction. The slightest obstacle, whatever it may be, a pin or a matchstick inserted at the lower edge of the construction, definitely upsets the general pattern. However, if the same obstacle is placed at the upper end, it does not create the same phenomenon.

One of Darchen's experiments clearly proves the teamwork involved here. A very thin metallic plaque is cut out so that it can be placed on the side of the honeycomb under construction, on the same level. This plaque, being of exactly the same dimensions as the bees' work, greatly disturbs them. All building stops on that side and the result is a monstrous asymmetrical comb.

In the second test, the metal plaque is introduced in the same way, but this time it is quite porous. Very shortly, it is completely covered over with wax by the workers, which use it as a foundation, and there is no upset at all in their work plan.

Darchen explains this in the following way: the regulation of the construtcion is effected by subtle alterations in the muscular tractions transmitted through the legs. Observation reveals to us that the waxmakers run their legs through the perforations of the porous metal plaque. From this contact, they therefore gain some "information," the exact nature of which we have yet to learn.

Later on, Darchen set a number of other complex problems for the waxmaking bees. In almost all cases, they showed they were capable of retouching a job so as to make it conform to the typical hive plan, which is passed on from generation to generation.

Queen bees play a very important role in the hive. Where construction is concerned, on the one hand they inhibit the making of royal cells and on the other accelerate that of workers' cells. It would seem that this is achieved through the spreading of a construction hormone emitted by the queen and pervading the entire society.

↑ THE TERMITE, BUILDER IN THE DARK

Work methods do not seem to be the same for all social insects. Termites have been carefully studied by Grassé.

Termites' nests are not made of wax but of masticated wood or of earth. They do not make regular cells, but a series of different cavities, each of which has its own use. Grassé was able to distinguish the collection of rooms in which the eggs are laid, those in which food stores are kept, and the royal chamber, in which the reigning couple lives, the father and mother of the whole colony.

In a second group came the galleries which prolong the nest at great distances underground and allow the termites to reach sources of food supplies as well as building materials without having to expose themselves to the light which they fear.

A third group, less understandable, is made up of cavities which open toward the outside, but which are not connected to the main nest and have no galleries leading to them. Finally, an empty space, a "sanitary vacuum," surrounds certain hills and separates them from the neighboring terrain. These latter cavities are deserted, and termites only rarely venture into them.

Obviously, it is out of the question to try to follow every phase of the construction work of such a complex; so the observer has had to be satisfied with a few scattered investigations. Termites have one peculiarity which makes the study easier. Normally, they flee from light and work in darkness, which makes observation very difficult, yet if one is able to separate a group of workers from their nest and get them into an enclosure where there are building materials at their disposal, they overcome their aversion to light and quickly start to build themselves a shelter. In this way, observation of the actions of a few individuals identified by colored marks has allowed a study of the principles on which their work is based.

The conclusions drawn from such study are rather extraordinary. The masons do not form into work teams, and the individual jobs are in no way coordinated with each other. On the other hand, they are coordinated in terms of the overall situation which leads each of the workers to manufacture little balls of mortar and place them on the ground. When the balls have become numerous enough, they in turn become a new stimulus which exerts an attraction and determines where the newly made mortar balls will be placed. This accumulation of mortar balls appears to be the starting point for pillars and walls. As these structures gradually emerge, they themselves become stimulating and direct the further acts of their builders. This rather paradoxical stimulation has been given the name of *stimergy* or "stimulating work."

During the course of the job, the stimuli change their values. We know that a pile of balls leads to the erection of a pillar. When this pillar has reached a given height, it is abandoned if there is another pillar nearby. In this case, the two erections curve towards each other and finally form an arch.

One question then arises: how does the blind worker know of the existence of another pillar near enough to form an arch? According to Grassé, it is by the sense of smell. The workers are able to judge, very exactly, the distance away of a source of odor; so there is nothing amazing about their receiving stimuli at a distance.

One other question arises: is there not singular waste in this method of dropping the "bricks" all over the work area and then building pillars and walls at those spots where the piles are highest? Even though it is dangerous to try to judge insect behavior in terms of our own norms, Grassé's writings seem to give a very satisfactory answer to this. The workers have a tendency to come back to the same spot to drop their mortar balls.

However, this is not an absolute rule: especially if the distance between the source of the building material and the work area is large, the worker will drop his load more or less at random. But the tendency does quite certainly exist, and it is enough to explain how the placement of the essential building elements is concentrated in one precise spot. Sometimes, the search for materials can lead the worker very far afield. In the Ubangi, termites have been known to go down almost fourteen yards to bring up clay. In the Sahara, termites of another species go all the way down to the phreatic layer—that is, tens of yards down into the earth—to get the water needed for their building. Finally, even though Grassé himself warns that "prudence advises us not to eliminate any possibility of cooperation or exchange of information between workers," stimergy can be accepted as an adequate explanation.

Some termitaries go above six yards in height and reach diameters of 33 yards. When there are a large number of them, they considerably alter the landscape, and, before the coming of man, the termitarium certainly represented the greatest modification any higher form of animal life had wrought in the natural aspect of life.

⚰ SEWING AND WEAVING

The *oecophylla* ants live in the tropics where they are very common, especially on coffee plantations. The nests of these ants are made of leaves held together by threads of silk. The ants have no silk glands and would be unable to build in this manner if their larvae did not have such organs. This silk which, in other species, is used only for the construction of cocoons, is here put to use by the adults. This is done very simply: while one team of workers, using legs and jaws, brings two leaves together, another comes up carrying a larva between its mandibles. It touches the edges of the leaves with the larva which each time secretes a bit of particularly adhesive silk. Then, like a weaver, using this living shuttle, the ant spins a solid web between the two leaves. At this point, the workers of the first team relax their pressure and leave for another part of the job. The two leaves remain solidly stuck together, for the adhesive is stronger than the materials themselves.

Chauvin, studying these ants on the Ivory Coast, made some curious observations. First, the building activities of the oecophylla are hard to discourage. Twelve times, with a pair of scissors, he cut the nest open, only to see the ants tirelessly repair the breach. Next, using a pair of tweezers, he picked up a team of workers and found that another group immediately replaced them, going into exactly the positions previously occupied by the others. It was necessary to take the scissors and cut away the edges of the leaves for the new arrivals to assume different positions.

Chauvin also studied the red woods ant which builds a dome-shaped nest. By following the work of 155 ants individually, Chauvin was able to note that one-half of the time they deposited their loads of twiglets on the sides of the dome, and the other half of the time at the top. Since the surface of the top is relatively small in relation to that of the base, no other result is possible but the formation of a cone.

As a last example of insect construction, let us consider the larvae of phryganea flies, well-known to anglers under the name of "wood carriers" or "load carriers." They owe this name to the protective tube they build for themselves in order to cover their defenseless bodies. The tubes, lined with silk, are built of widely varying materials according to the species. They may be of tiny gravel, bits of leaves, or sprigs of wood.

Biologists have never been reluctant to bother these insects in order to gain further knowledge. A larva taken out of its shelter will seek refuge in any tube of the right size, but will quickly withdraw from a glass tube. Older larvae can very well tell the difference between their own shelters and others of the same size and the same apparent aspect. When a shelter is damaged, it is repaired with the usual materials, unless the break is very tiny, in which case it is repaired with silk.

IS INSTINCT MORE INTELLIGENT THAN INTELLIGENCE?

We will now have a look at what happens among vertebrates.

Curiously enough, higher animals build neither more nor better than their inferiors. Could the awakening of intelligence blunt the flowering of instinct?

Some fish build relatively complex nests. The small stickleback braids aquatic grass to form a ball which will protect its eggs. Some batrachians, although it is rather rare, make starts toward nests. Birds, of course, are the masters at this craft, and some of their nests are true masterpieces—for instance, those of the seamstress warbler or those of the weaverbirds, made of fibers braided together with extraordinary care.[1]

Among mammals, we know of a bat which builds a sort of tent by using cut-up palm leaves. There are also burrows of all sorts,

[1] We are not lacking in very careful studies of how birds build their nests. Kortland thus studied in Holland the building of a nest by a cormorant. Friedmann devoted himself to the fascinating problem of how the weaverbirds of Africa make their knots.

some of which have plans of great complexity. There are still a few other more or less rough types of buildings, such as muskrats' huts or harvest rats' little grass nests, but especially there is the work of the beavers.

Beaver dams, whether they be of small dimensions or go across rivers several tens of yards wide, are something to strike the imagination.[2] They are usually connected with the beaver's cabin and are really only intended to create an area of calm water of an even level around this habitat. In this way, the beaver creates protection for its home, the entrance to which remains constantly under water. Thus it is possible to bring to the work area the wood which is both the basic food of the animal and his building material.

For many years, a distinction was made between two types of beavers: the hutmaking or builder beaver, and the burrowing beaver, which could do nothing but burrow into a riverbank.

French beavers were supposed to be burrowers. Some claimed that, within memory of man, no beaver had ever built anything in France. This assertion was undoubtedly wrong, for traces of quite old beaver dams have been found here and there throughout the country. But such activity must have been very rare, and this fact seemed to justify the hypothesis of those who claimed that, under the pressure of the hunt and systematic destruction, the beavers had lost their builder instinct. A short time before the war, however, a forester named Cordier-Goni, having put a beaver into a park where it was in complete safety, was amazed to see it start building a hut. Beavers being legally protected in France, as in many other countries, it was therefore possible to anticipate that they might start building dams and huts on waterways.

In 1947, a beaver dam on a small subtributary of the Rhone was reported, and, since 1954, a biologist, Richard, has been studying the constructions of beavers in France. It would in fact have been most surprising if an instinctive behavior had been able to get lost so easily, for the few hundred years which separate us from the Middle Ages and the time when beavers teemed in the region of Paris are only a very little step in the life of a species.

---

[2] On the Jefferson River, in the United States, beavers built a dam 700 yards long and almost seven yards wide which a horseman could ride across with ease.

✓

CHAPTER X

Art and the Animal

✓

IS man the only one who can have esthetic feelings or, on the contrary, is this aptitude widely spread throughout nature? This question has provoked many a controversy. Romanes, who was the accepted authority on animal psychology around 1880, thought that the taste for colorful display in birds was a proof of their esthetic sense.

Later, after serious study of the question, it was agreed that no artistic emotion whatever was to be found in animals. No one takes the joy expressed by the singing bird, the sophisticated form of a nest, or the shrewdly choreographed nuptial dances to be premises of art.

Not so long ago there was still wonder about the behavior of gardener birds, already discussed briefly in Chapter I. The tales told by the first travelers who landed on the coasts of New Guinea and Australia made mention of small cabins decorated with taste and surrounded by gardens in which clumps of fruit trees, flowers, and strange rock arrangements made quite surprising ornamental displays. It was soon discovered that these were not the work of human beings, but of a relative of the bird of paradise, the gardener bird.

In this group, the bowerbirds, *ptilonorhynchidae,* are no doubt the most interesting to study. For a part of the year, they live in wandering bands, and it is only in the month of May that the adult males decide to choose solitude. From then on, they go in for intensive prospecting, and, after having found a suitable place, they get to work. With interlaced branches, they build arbors. The axis of the construction is always set on a north-south line, the angle of deviation from which never exceeds 30 degrees. At one end of the arbor, on a well-cleared surface, the bird lays out a number of varicolored objects. In the case of the bowerbirds, the chosen objects are always blue, yellow-green, brown or gray; they are mostly feathers, flowers, fruits, snailshells, and mushrooms. But sometimes, the bowerbird does even better; he paints his construction with crushed fruits, the purple pulp of which gives it a very dark tone; sometimes, when he is able, he mixes charcoal into this paste and thus gets an even darker coloring. It even happens that these birds use a kind of "paintbrush" to spread the concoction on.

Other gardener birds do not build arbors made of two parallel walls joined by a vault at the top, but veritable circular huts, the walls of which surround a central mast. A very large entryway allows one to see what is going on inside.

The construction of the brown gardener is particularly remarkable, for this bird decorates his structure with living orchids, which continue to grow and give the hut a truly extraordinary appearance. The garden is equally carefully planned; vividly colored flowers and fruits are piled up, arranged with a definite feel for symmetry. The Queensland gardener builds a hut of the same type which, if it is less well decorated, is just as remarkable because of its size. It may exceed three yards in height. Finally, one other bird of this family is content with merely decorating a pillar made of one sapling and surrounding it with a circular trail which is totally cleared off. In this last case, the whole thing looks rather like a Christmas tree.

The gardener bird.

As might have been expected, this strange behavior became the subject of extended arguments between specialists. Some maintained that the essential motivation of these constructions was of an esthetic and conscious nature. Others felt that these phenomena should be looked on as a sort of game. In the last analysis it was decided that they must be part of sexual behavior; the true significance of the entire apparatus of the constructions and the gardens and displays associated with them would appear to be the male's desire to attract the female.

The relationship between the construction activities and the conditioning of the male sexual glands is now established, and a painstaking study of these birds reveals that all their work, including the north-south direction of the arbor, is intended to show off the sexual valor of the male who struts about his garden displaying his collections, picks up some precious piece in his beak, and rearranges it on another clump of his domain.

It is undoubtedly sexual behavior, but does that mean that there cannot be an esthetic component in it as well? This is a question which is difficult to answer. Only the bird himself could decide this for us, we have to admit. While it appears certain that there is nothing about this behavior which might be called art for art's sake, it is no less true that many questions remain unanswered, particularly those concerning what pleasure the animals can derive from carrying out these complicated actions.

⚡ THE ENIGMA OF ANIMAL PAINTERS

If we want to talk about animal art, there is another aspect of the problem we must consider. Alongside the studies made of animals living in their natural habitat, let us look at the ones carried out in laboratories.

A recent work by an English naturalist tells us a great deal about apes who draw and paint. The book, by Desmond Morris, entitled *The Biology of Art,* first describes the amazement in England when a London art gallery devoted an exhibit to paintings done by chimpanzees. It then describes the work of American psychologists, the Kelloggs, who, it seems, were the first to make scientific observations of the graphic aptitudes of simians. In order to have a basis of comparison, they raised their own son along with a she-monkey.

They made several discoveries, among which was that a chimpanzee can scribble if shown how and that this scribbling soon becomes a spontaneous activity. However, there is one basic difference: the child's drawing quickly becomes representational while the simian's never does.

Other authors had previously noted that monkeys were capable of drawing. Toward 1916, the Russian psychologist Kohts attempted a serious study of the subject and found, among other things, that the early scribbles of a monkey can develop and undergo changes.

Since then, experimental studies have increased. The names of the artists have been revealed. Among them, Alpha, the chimpanzee of the Yerkes Laboratory, Congo of the London Zoo, Beth and Tom of the Baltimore Zoo,[1] Alexander, an orang-utang, and Sophie, a gorilla of the Rotterdam Zoo, have made a name for themselves; even monkeys of the lower orders have gotten into the running, such as Pablo, a capuchin studied by Rensch at the University of Munster, and other monkeys of the same species studied in Moscow by Mme Kohts. In all, Morris's book accounts for the artistic accomplishments of 32 simians, including 23 chimpanzees, 2 gorillas, 3 orangutangs, and 4 capuchins. The most industrious of all was undoubtedly Congo, who was responsible for over 400 paintings.

Betsy, a young female chimpanzee of the Baltimore Zoo, went into art on a commercial basis. A few years ago, nearly 70 paintings by this "master" were sold, one of them bringing $75. The money she earned was used to buy Betsy a husband.

The comparative study of the drawings and daubings of the monkeys allowed Morris to isolate six essential principles, which we shall consider one by one.

---

[1] Drawings made by Tom and Beth were shown to psychologists who specialized in the interpretation of children's drawings. Tom's work was judged to be clearly characterized. It revealed, the specialist said, a boy of seven to eight years, with aggressive paranoid tendencies. As for Beth's, it was interpreted as coming from a girl of about ten of the schizoid type. The psychologists had not been wrong about the sexes of their subjects and, after all, we have no way of knowing whether the monkeys in questions were as mentally healthy as all that!

⸱ CREATIVE ART

First, the principle of self-rewarding activity. The animal finds his reward in the pleasure of drawing itself. He does not hide his discontent when he is disturbed, and there were cases of very mild animals biting their masters who tried to interfere with their work. This was carried further. One researcher tried to associate the drawing with a reward. Very quickly, the monkey understands that any kind of scribble at all will earn him a banana, and he loses all interest in the character of his work, whereas those simians who work only for the pleasure of accomplishment try very hard and make indubitable efforts to bring perfection to what they have undertaken.

Second principle: that of composition. A feeling for balanced masses and for rhythm in the image undoubtedly exists in monkeys. In all cases, the monkey shows a definite tendency to do one central figure and stick with that only. Sometimes, the execution of a new figure, a spiral for instance, literally fascinates him to such a point that he seems to ignore the rest of the blank page before him. Moreover, great differences can be noted between animals even when they belong to the same species. Congo liked to draw figures that had the shape of fans while Alpha never did this. In the same way, the tendency to want to complete a figure begun by the experimenter or to center the composition around one detail already drawn on the sheet is subject to wide variations.

The third principle is that of calligraphic differentiation. Morris considers that graphic development of the splotches or lines is made in spurts, but that the monkey (like the child,[2] incidentally) discovers forms in a slow and continuous process. Morris then goes into the principle of variations on a theme. It seems that the animal takes a true pleasure in exploring the field of such variations and that he studies the effect created by the slightest changes. The

[2] Experiments concerning simian art have been carried out almost exclusively with young monkeys. The only adult to have been studied was the chimpanzee Jonny. He went into a state of intense sexual excitement whenever he painted or drew. It is not known whether such a reaction was peculiar to Jonny or would be shared by other adult males. The latter are usually overlooked by experimenters: their lack of docility is too well-known, as well as the violence of some of their reactions.

The expression: almost that of a man, yet not a man.
An African monkey.—Photo John Gajda

whole work therefore retains a family feeling, what might be called a style.

Another principle was isolated by Morris, that of optimum heterogeneity, meaning that the work of art starts with extreme homogeneity, the blank sheets of paper, to go on toward a greater and greater heterogeneity. The maximum of heterogeneity, that is to say the proliferation of detail, is not necessarily what is desired, and the artist should, in theory, be able to feel when his work is completed. This consciousness is very clear in certain monkeys. Several times, Congo was seen to grow very angry because he was urged to go on with a drawing which he considered completed, and, to show his disdain for this additional work imposed on him, he drew lines in all directions as if he were trying to cross out his work.

Rather curiously, if the monkey respects the law of optimum heterogeneity where the line is concerned, he has no regard for it in the selection of colors, and he uses all the shades put at his disposal indiscriminately and without thrift. In man, something quite different takes place. The more primitive of arts use only a minimum number of colors, even when there are no technical difficulties in getting many more.

Finally, Morris brings out the principle of universal imagery. The classical example is that of the rectangle governed by the golden number. When people are given a free choice between rectangles of different proportions, more than a third will choose the one having the proportion of 1:1.618, and the others choose closely approximating shapes. This taste, it would seem, is connected with the formation of our visual field, and persons born one-eyed, it is said, prefer a simple square.

The profound resemblances to be seen in the production of different monkey artists attest to the fact that this law holds true for them, too. The universality of tastes may go even further.

Often it is difficult to define the borderline between esthetic feeling and curiosity. A chimpanzee is able to look at a picture book for a very long time, and it becomes very difficult to get him away from the contemplation of a kaleidoscope. But if curiosity is evident here, no research has as yet informed us whether the ape has a preference for certain figures or certain forms.

Rensch offered various animals cards set up in pairs. On one, there is a regular, symmetrical drawing; on the other an irregular asymmetrical design. Animals, all being very curious by nature, lose little time in coming near and taking up one of the cards in their paws or beaks. Rensch assumes the postulate that the card taken first is the one that is preferred. Hundreds of tests were made for each pair, and statistical calculations were then made with a view to establishing preferences. It was found that, given eight pairs of different cards, eight times the capuchin monkey will select the symmetrical design. The long-tailed cercopithecus will make the same choice only five times, the crow six times, although in the remaining two cases it shows no preference at all. The jackdaw also takes the symmetrical shape six times out of eight, while showing no preference one time and one time selecting the asymmetrical figure.

There are therefore esthetic tastes common to a great number of species, and it may not be by chance or just by habit that we react to the song of a bird or the perfect formation of a nest, for our tastes and our colors have biological roots which it would be useless to try to deny.

Design is a biological function, it seems, common to all the primates.

✓

The Senses We Lack

✓

MANY of the questions we ask about animals' performances will be answered the day the animal kingdom reveals to us the secrets of its sense capacities.

✓ THE INAUDIBLE VOICE OF THE BAT

Recent work has brought many wholesale upsets in this area, but there are still many open questions. Bats, for instance, are among the most irritating of animals. As early as 1794, the naturalist Spallanzini was able to demonstrate that bats guided themselves by their hearing. At that time, it was believed that they reacted only to sounds audible to man, and it took a long time to find out that some bats could guide themselves and locate their prey by way of a sound system made up of frequencies inaudible to us.

It was in 1938 that American biologists first recorded the voices of bats; since then, many researchers have studied the performances of these animals, particularly their amazing ability to avoid obstacles in the most complete darkness. Wires of only 1/60th of an inch in diameter, strung vertically in a room with a space between them barely exceeding the wingspan, in no case offer any kind of bothersome obstacle to bats, who fly about in all directions missing them as if they were not there.

But it is when they are chasing after flying insects that bats use their "radar," or rather their "sonar," with the greatest adeptness.[1]

[1] Sonar (or asdic) is based on the following principle: a high-frequency sound signal is emitted, and the time between the emission and the return of the echo, since we know the speed of sound, allows one to calculate the distance between the emitter and the reflecting object. Sonar was created and perfected during the world wars for use in the antisubmarine struggle.

The owl, which flies at night without bumping into trees, possesses a very special kind of vision.—Photo Holmes-Lebel

They very easily capture insects as tiny as mosquitoes (and always in the deepest darkness) at the rate of no less than one every ten seconds.

In most cases, the hunter bat pays no attention to the sounds emitted by its victim but sweeps the air with its own ultrasonic emission and is guided by the echo that bounces back.

Films shot in infrared, in order not to upset the behavior of the animals too much, have given us a visualization of the extraordinary precision of this mechanism. It occasionally happens that the insect is missed on the first assault, but the flight pattern is corrected and the second time around the insect is invariably caught. Motion pictures have even shown that when the prey is missed the bat can catch the insect with the end of its wing and toss it with precision toward its mouth.

Although highly developed, the bat's hunting technique is not such that there can be no defense against it. Some millers perceive the ultrasonic emissions of their enemies, and when they do they stop flying and let themselves drop to the ground.

An English physiologist, J. D. Pye, has properly compared the bat to a self-guiding missile of remarkable efficiency, fuel for which is supplied by its targets themselves.

But no present-day missile is capable of some of the performances which seem elementary games to these animals.

We know that they can hunt under conditions which, transposed to another plane, would cause insurmountable difficulty for humans. For instance, the bat can carry on its hunt in very heavy rain and get along very well, making no error in distinguishing the raindrops from insects of approximately the same size.

Let us also give thought to the difficulty of hunting in a forest thick with intertwining branches, foliage, and blossoms. Nor should we lose sight of the fact that bats are gregarious animals, living in groups sometimes numbering thousands of individuals. In a densely populated cave, the background noise, for one equipped to perceive hyperfrequencies, must be absolutely unbearable. Besides that, it must be difficult for the bat to distinguish its own echoes from that background noise, and yet collisions rarely, if ever, happen.

Griffin set animals aflight in rooms in which sound was being emitted that was up to 30,000 times stronger than that made by the animals. Despite it all, the bats could still get through the vertically strung wires, and their system for locating their quarry still operated perfectly. These facts, moreover, drew acousticists' attention to the efficiency of a group of receivers in comparison to a single one in what the technicians have come to call the "cocktail party effect," this self-explanatory name being used to designate the picking out of one specific sound from numerous other sounds, all of the same frequency.

⚡ TWO METHODS OF SPOTTING

Two families of chiroptera have been studied on this score, the vespertillions and rhinolophids, two families which use markedly different methods of spotting.

Those of the first family absolutely have to have both ears to make a correct spotting, for if one of these organs is put out of service the animal is as lost as if he were totally deaf. In the animals of this group, the ears are not mobile; moreover, these animals emit a great number of cries, very short and in modulated frequencies.

The rhinolophids, on the other hand, emit longer individual cries, less numerous, and in a constant frequency. They can get along very well with only one ear, the horn of which has a very special mobility; finally, they concentrate the sound emission in a narrow band which allows them to sweep the horizon and detect potential obstacles or quarry at relatively great distances.

⚡ WHAT HAPPENS UNDER WATER?

Some fish use similar, and others diametrically opposed, mechanisms to find their way through dark waters.

The Mexican characin, which lives in caves, is blind, but that does not keep it from getting around very well. We have recently learned that it uses the receivers of its lateral line to locate the reflections of waves of pressure created by its own movements.

It has also recently been proved that certain electric fish have quite remarkable spotting systems. Their organs produce impulses, and their receivers are perfectly able to detect the variations of impedance created by obstacles distorting the electrical field around the animal. In the same way, the electrical field of a congener can be detected with equal ease.

The nocturnal bird does make use of his infrared vision to capture a mouse.

An owl attacking.—Photos Rapho

However, in the depths of the sea, it would seem that mammals are the ones which have the most highly perfected detection and navigation systems—dolphins, for instance.

A highly developed navigational system, it should be pointed out, is almost a vital necessity to these animals. They move along at a high rate of speed, which has often been overestimated, but it is still a fact that they easily reach a speed of about twenty miles per hour. This very honorable performance, the dolphin's muscular power being what it is, requires a very highly developed hydro-dynamism. A collision with a rock at twenty miles per hour would be a serious accident, and dolphins have a penchant for rivermouths where waters are rather murky, just as they hunt at great depths where light is very slight.

The fact that dolphins make sounds has been known since men first took to the sea. Pliny and Aristotle mentioned it, and all sailors know the sounds the animals make, sounds which they have compared to the squeaking of mice.

Recordings made in the last few years have revealed curious similarities between these sounds and the ones made by sonar installed on ships. In the one case as in the other, a part of the emission is in the ultrasonic area, and both are made up of a rapid succession of clearly characterized impulses.

However, there are some differences. Dolphin emissions are in varied frequencies while those of sonar are constant. In the same way, the intensity of the signals emitted by the animals is also very variable while those of our installations are even. The fact that the sounds emitted constantly change in character and in volume allows spotting at very short range. What the dolphins have in fact is FM sonar. There is every chance that the returning echo will be different from the sound then being emitted, and when the start and return of the emission are very close together, it appreciably simplifies the gauging of distance.

Though we have mentioned only the dolphin—or, rather, dolphins, since there are many species of them—it should not be imagined that other cetaceans are without this faculty. Whales, cachalots, porpoises, and so on, most certainly all have very similar spotting systems which still remain to be studied. We already know that these animals emit sounds, some of which we have been able to record.

As we know most about them, we will therefore stick to dolphins. The most important research on dolphins has been done with funds supplied by the U.S. Navy. It has borne its fruit: we are now familiar with dolphin emissions, we know how they are made, what organs are used, and we have precise ideas about the performance this strange animal may be capable of.

In fact, dolphins are very fashionable animals right now, and while many are studying their language, others are trying to decipher the secrets of their detection processes. A recent work by Kellogg has very fortunately brought all of this up to date.

KELLOGG'S EXPERIMENTS

These experiments were carried on at the University of Florida marine laboratory, in a tank somewhat over 22 yards long and about 20 yards wide. At one end of the tank there are two "cages" in which a dolphin can be kept. Three mechanical installations were made, allowing the use of various apparatus, both on the surface of the water and underneath. There was a raft, a tackle, and a network of cables installed about five yards above the water.

Kellogg first studied the reactions of the animals to various submerged objects. A hydrophone allowed the recording of acoustical reactions, and the various tests were made first in clear and then in artificially troubled water.

The immersion of a yard-long metal bar brings an immediate sound reaction, but the dolphin neither moves nor tries to flee. A model simulating the shape of a fish: sound reaction, but again no movement. A real fish: repeated sound signals and approach. A man swimming in the pool: flight.

When food is thrown to the dolphins, the "plop" of the fish hitting the water is enough, it seems, to attract them, and they need no other leads to find it. But if the fish is slipped quietly into the water, the situation is not the same.

Sight does not necessarily play a role, as has been shown by the series of tests carried out in troubled waters. As for smell, dolphins simply have no sense of it. Taste does not appear to be of any great help to them either. This leaves us their famous sonar. And that sonar appears to be far better than the kind humans have invented. Our mechanisms seem unable to tell the difference between a wooden ship and a metal ship, and they will often take a whale for a submarine, or vice versa. The dolphin's sonar allows him to tell the difference between two fish of the same size but of different species. Many experiments prove this. If two fish are put in the water at the same time, which have different degrees of attractiveness for the dolphin, he will always go after the one he likes best, even in troubled waters or in deepest darkness. Kellogg also gave the dolphins their choice between a piece of fish and a piece of plastic of the same shape. In every case, they went straight for the piece of fish and deliberately ignored the plastic.

SEEING THE INVISIBLE

Another set of experiments tested their ability to avoid invisible obstacles.

Kellogg gave a dolphin a choice between two fish. One was swimming in free water, the other behind a glass pane. Both pieces of bait were offered through narrow windows in a metallic wall. In every case, the dolphin went after the free-swimming fish and made no effort to get at the other.

Similarly, the pool may be strung with a veritable maze of nets, metallic stems, and other obstacles. At the "plop" of the fish at the other end of the pool, the dolphin rushes toward it, maneuvering his way rapidly through the series of obstacles, apparently without the least bit of trouble.

Finally, Kellogg tried to upset the dolphins by sending sound waves through the water which would interfere with their sonar waves. The most effective jamming sound, it was imagined, would be the rebroadcasting of recordings of the sounds made by the animals themselves. This was done within a particularly complex maze, but the jamming in no way appeared to bother the dolphins, which were not upset on hearing their own past sounds.

As with bats, we find in these animals a remarkable example of echo location that can hardly be jammed. While the usefulness of such an ability may be evident, since both bats and dolphins live in groups, the nature of the mechanism itself still remains most mysterious and has left researchers at a loss. Moreover, all the other sounds tried out by Kellogg to fool the dolphins proved totally ineffectual.

Much behavior that is mysterious to us can thus be explained only by the use of senses we do not know of. Sometimes, however, the disparities with our own faculties are very slight and call into play perceptions which we can perfectly well imagine, even though they be different from our own.

In this regard, the bee is often mentioned, for its sight has been carefully studied. This insect's sharpness of vision is only one-tenth that of a man and, moreover, it has astigmatism. The bee has good color perception, but not in the same range as ours, for it cannot see red while it perceives ultraviolet as a color. It also has a much higher frequency of vision than we do, so that our motion pictures running at 24 images per second must appear to it as a succession of still pictures, and our light bulbs fed in alternating current at 50 cycles must flicker strangely before its eyes. For the bee to get the same impression as a human being in one or the other of these cases, the frequency would have to reach 300 per second.

If we add that the bee can see the polarization plane of light, we have more or less completed the picture of this insect's optics.

But all of the secrets of insects' sight have not yet been fathomed —far from it. Most insects have, in addition to their complex eyes, a variable number of simple eyes, known as ocelli. Just what these organs do is still quite mysterious. We know that ants, bees, and flies no longer react to light and act like blind animals if their ocelli are covered over, even though their eyes remain intact. However, it has been demonstrated in other insects that objects passing before the ocelli provoke no electrical activity.

Some insects are even more disconcerting to us. The notonectidae, for instance. These aquatic bugs are able to locate very efficiently a source of vibrations, such as those coming from quarry. They are able to tell the difference between two sources situated only

7 to 9 degrees apart, and the receiving organ which can make this judgment is made up of the rows of hairs growing on their third pair of legs.

A number of theories have been advanced to explain the performance of the notonectidae. It was at first believed that their organs could perceive the phase differences of the wave successively striking first one then the other of its receivers, but that would only apply to a single frequency, and the insect's quarries give off vibrations much too varied for this.

The intensity theory holds that, the organ being on the other side of the body from the source of the vibrations, it could perceive a lowering of intensity, but the insect is not corpulent enough to create an appreciable difference after so short a course. Subjective intensity has also been considered. It is held that the intensity is more or less great according to whether or not the receiver is in the direction of the source. But in the case of the notonectidae, the receiving organ does not appear sufficiently localized; it does not seem to be directionalized and constantly changes position since it moves along with the legs.

Finally, there is the "delay" theory which has not convinced everyone. The organ being on the side opposite to the sound would perceive it with a slight delay. By moving in a zigzag, the notonectid would always be at an angle in relation to the source and in this way would increase the delay compared to what it would be if the approach were made in a straight line.

The bee's eye perceives a strange world, very different from ours.
—Photo Guy Dhuit

⌁ NEITHER SIGHT NOR HEARING, NOR ANYTHING KNOWN

One rather extraordinary example of a "mysterious sense" is the case of the sirex. The larva of this hymenopter lives and undergoes its transformation within dead wood; the fully formed insect then finds its way out, always going by the shortest route. How can the sirex know the exact direction? In the last century, Fabre classified the data of what he called the sirex problem, and nothing adduced since then has offered a satisfactory solution.

We can therefore do no better than to go directly back to Fabre:

"The exit compass exists, there is no doubt, both for the larvae preparing their way to liberation and the adult sirex obliged to work its own way out.

"What is it? Here the problem sinks into a darkness which is perhaps impenetrable; we are not well enough equipped in methods of impression even to suspect what causes guide the animal. This is, in certain ways, another world of the senses in which our organs perceive nothing, a world that is closed to us.

"The eye of the camera obscura sees the invisible and photographs the image of the ultraviolet; the tympanum of the microphone hears what to us is silence. A physics toy, a chemical compound are more sensitive than we. Would it be foolhardy to attribute similar aptitudes to the insect's delicate organization, even concerning agents unknown to our science because they are not within the domain of our own senses? To this question, there can be no positive answer; we have suspicions, and nothing more. But let us at least eliminate certain false ideas which might occur to us.

"Does the wood, through its structure, guide the animal, adult or larva? Gnawed against the grain, it must make an impression of one sort; gnawed along the grain, it must make another. Could that not be enough to guide the borer? No, because in a fallen stump, the emergence is made according to the degree of proximity of light, sometimes by horizontal section in a straight line running along the length of the grain, sometimes along the side in a curved line slicing across the grain. Is this compass an electrical, chemical, or thermal influence, or yet some other kind? No, for in a standing tree trunk the exit can be made as well to the north, which is constantly in shadow, as to the south, sunbathed all the day. The opening is made toward the side where the distance is shortest, without other consideration. Could it be temperature? No more so, for the shady side, which is chillier, is used as well as the one exposed to the sun.

"Could it be sound? Not that either. What sound, in the silence of solitude? And besides, do rumbles from the outside have a different propagation through one centimeter of wood more or less?

"Could it be gravity? Not always, for the poplar trunk shows us various sirexes moving upside down, head downward, without in any way changing the outline of their curve.

"Then what is this guide? I have no idea."

(Entomological Memoirs, Series 4)

A large insect of the ichneumon group, the rhyssa, lays its eggs in the larvae of certain wood borers. The operation involves two technical impossibilities—that is, impossibilities in terms of human technics. The rhyssa succeeds in locating the coveted larva through two and one-half inches of pine wood and then is able to penetrate the wood with a flexible wimble or borer which is no thicker than a horsehair.

How can it find its goal? The mystery remains total.

Photographs have often been made of the activities of this brown and yellow insect flying about in a pine woods, landing on a stump, and, with a thousand precautions, plunging its borer into the wood. Once the insect has left, an examination of the stump always reveals a plump larva in which first the egg and then the larva of the rhyssa will develop.

The most fantastic hypotheses have been suggested to explain this mystery. Some believe it is all done with vibrations. But it is hard to conceive what vibrations might come from a fatty and virtually amorphous larva. Odor has also been alleged, but it would have to be a strong one to come through two and one-half inches of wood and not be overpowered by the much stronger scent of the sap.

Yet, in this area it would be foolhardy to eliminate arbitrarily any hypothesis whatsoever, for surprises are only too frequent. As far as the sharpness of the insect's sense of smell is concerned, if laboratory experiments do not always reveal any extraordinary superiority in relation to our own, observations made in the field contradict these findings. All too often attempts have been made to measure sensibility with substances which have no great significance for the animal. If, on the other hand, we study its reactions to substances which have a basic biological interest for it, the results are so amazing as to change our whole conception of the matter.

✓ TO FIND A MATE

This is so with tests made with the sexual substances of butterflies, the females of which, as we have known for a long time, can attract the males even at very great distances.

An experience of Labonnefon quite some time ago shows the insistence with which male millers seek out their females. Having caught a female of the great nightpeacock, Labonnefon soon found the room he was in invaded by males rushing in through the open window. They became so numerous that the overwhelmed lepidopterologist had to close that way of access. A short time later, he heard wings beating in an old cold stove in the room. He opened it, and several males flew out of the trap, into which the feminine effluvium had attracted them by the only possible way in, the chimney!

Standfuss, having put in his garden a female *saturnia pavonia,* was able to attract 127 males of the species in a matter of six hours. These butterflies were marked and released at different distances away. At 2½ miles 40 per cent were able to get back to the female. At 7½ miles, 26 per cent were still able to make it.

In 1922, Mell carried out the same experiment with another butterfly, the *artias selene,* and got spectacular returns from a point located seven miles away. These results led certain authors to believe that there was more involved than just olfactory attraction.

Many observations have shown that males sometimes arrived riding on the wind, instead of flying into the wind, as would have been more logical if they had simply been following the trail of an aroma. Other experiments showed that the female could be placed among the most violent conflicting odors without in any way interfering with the arrival of her suitors.[1]

[1] The performances of butterflies are the more amazing because laboratory experiments have shown how nearly identical its sense of smell is to that of man. Man's is even sharper in very many cases. We can detect .000,000,4 mg.

In this way was born the hypothesis that the sexual substance must propagate waves of some kind: the supposed radiation would then act as the basis for the stimulus. A short time after the last war, this theory found a certain amount of acceptance. Two American entomologists, Beck and Miles, claimed that females enclosed in inaccessible receptacles could still exercise their attraction on males on the outside. They placed various screens between the females and the males and got some strange results with filters which cut out infrared rays. According to them, the male by sending out an infrared ray could detect the aroma of an object by the reflection spectrum of the said object, which would mean the existence of yet another animal radar.

It must be admitted, however, that these experiments were not followed up on, and had only a passing acknowledgment. The mystery of the male butterflies' powers of detection has still not been cleared up, despite one more attempt to explain it. It has been held that the habit of flying in ever-widening concentric circles might explain the return of the butterflies to the female. It is true that wide-wing-spanned butterflies do seem to fly this way, but their cruising speed is low, barely six miles an hour, and a quick calculation shows that even if they widened their radius by a mile each time around, it would still take them a very long time to get back close to the female. Before having completed six circles, the poor butterfly would have covered over 60 miles, and the night would be over without his having had a chance to turn it into a wedding night.

Even if, as Le Magnen has so correctly written, the wave hypothesis remains completely without substantiation, while there are many proofs of the molecular character of the olfactory stimulus, it is no less true that, in the present state of science, there is still no irrefutable explanation of the Mell and Standfuss experiments.

OTHER ACCOMPLISHMENTS

Other animals have often amazed those who observed them.

In fish, there is a special nervous formation known as the "lateral line" which is particularly sensitive to vibrations. A fish which is

---

per liter of skatole whereas the geotrupe dung beetle detects this matter only at a concentration of .003 mg. per liter. Ammonia is detectable to the housefly above a level of .04 mg. per liter, whereas we are aware of this substance at a concentration below .035 per liter.

blind but has its lateral line intact can move about without difficulty and very easily evade the hand that tries to grasp it. On the other hand, a blind fish with a partly damaged lateral line bumps into obstacles and is easy to grasp. The lateral line therefore seems to allow the fish to perceive both moving and motionless objects by means of soundings.

Among the mysterious senses, we may also mention that of being sensitive to electric fields. According to Schua, a golden hamster will move his young away if his nest is placed within an electric field by an experimenter.

Police dogs after careful training become capable of following trails with a flair which seems prodigious. Efforts have been made to determine the limits of this ability to discriminate between sometimes very similar odors. A British writer, Kaimus, asked himself to what extent a police dog might be able to tell the difference in the odors of twins. The subjects were twins who had always lived together and doubtless had scents which would be rather hard to tell apart. In a first experiment, the twins went off, arm in arm, then separated at a given point. The dog, which had had the clothing of one of them given to him to smell, then took off. He quickly picked up the trail, and, when he got to the parting-point, without much hesitation he followed the trail of the one to whom the clothes belonged.

In another experiment, the dog was deceived in the following manner: one of the twins walked off alone; having gotten to the given point, he was met by a car from which his brother got out. He got in, and the brother continued the walk in his place. The dog was made to smell the clothing of the first walker and then released. In this case, the dog was taken in and he stayed with the trail, totally unaware of the substitution. This would seem to indicate the limits to the police dog's abilities.

But here again we must point out that the motivation in a laboratory experiment is not the same as in a real-life situation. The police dog in a criminal investigation is not placed in the same position as in a scientific experiment, and no one can tell what influence this environment may have on his behavior.

Another chapter could be written about what might be done with animals' extraordinary sensitivity.

The olfactory sensitivity of fish is so extraordinary that it has been possible to use them to detect infinitesmal traces of certain substances in polluted waters. A fish can be trained to show certain reactions by conditioning to chemical substances. The bluntnose minnow can learn to differentiate between phenol (associated with food distribution) and para-chlorophenol (associated with punishment): it can tell the two apart easily even when the dilution is down to 5 ten-thousandths. Similarly, another very common minnow can detect eugenol at a dilution of 17 one-millionths and phenylethyl alcohol at 23 one-millionths.

There are almost 10,000 different species of insects which use a song as their method of sexual attraction. Specialists have naturally wondered how it was possible to make out which song belonged to a given insect. Studies made through recordings have allowed the establishing of catalogues of the indispensable songs and the classifying of different sound emissions.

In an extension of this, it has been suggested that the receiving organs of certain insects might be kept alive after their owners and used to equip cosmic reconnaissance apparatus. The range potential of these organs might well be magnified and then used to issue commands to other mechanisms or else as detectors.

All of this opens up new vistas: if the universe as we know it is the result of sensations recorded by our sense organs, it would seem quite certain that other organs would record a different universe.

But even if this were the only difference between man and animal, there would be a very difficult barrier to get across. Our technics allow us to make use of a few additional senses, but a man does not use them 24 hours out of 24, and generally he does so only through the intermediary of one of his other senses.

A radar operator watches the screen on which the information appears much more than he actually makes use of his apparatus. The commando who moves at night by means of an infrared light only uses it from time to time. But if we speculate that some day we might be able to "graft" one or another of these extensions to the nervous system of man, an entire restructuring of our psychic nature would be the result.

✓

The Strange Story of
Animal Calculators

✓

EDUCATED animals are a frequent attraction of circuses and fairs. We often see a dog or a horse which can count or do simple calculations by striking with its foot while everyone applauds. But in general this is not a very exciting act. In less sophisticated times, however, animal calculators were very popular with audiences, and even aroused the curiosity of the scientific world.

The question of animal calculators is for many the kind of forbidden subject which must be kept out of any scientific literature. Hediger makes reference to "the idiotic legend of dogs and horses who express themselves by striking blows."

It must be admitted that the writings of the people who believed in the mathematical faculties of animals are not without naïveté. Professor Gustav Wolf, a Basel psychiatrist, wrote on this subject in 1914: "Once again something truly great, something overwhelming, has been accomplished outside the limits of organized science. And, as with everything that is new, it has to fight against the dogmas of the school and the Church."

We have tried to show that behind the hoax or practical joke quality of these phenomena there is hidden a truth which might be worthy of study.

Of course, nine times out of ten, the whole thing is faked, and, while the trainer may impress us by having been able to pull it off, the performance nonetheless remains a commonplace event. However, in some cases, even the most meticulous investigations have been unable to turn up any trickery, and when that happens the act becomes something of real interest.

ᵧ THE ELBERFELD HORSES

The most famous of all the unexplained cases is that of the horses of Elberfeld, in Germany. At the turn of the century, a horse fancier named Wilhelm von Osten trained his animals with special refinements and, among other accomplishments, he tried to teach them to count. In very short order, a stallion called Hans showed himself adept at it. At the beginning, a random number was set out on an easel; and Hans, tapping on a sort of wooden stool, the tens with his right hoof, and the digits with his left, would identify the numbers written.

He was also taught to read by this process. He beat his hoof in a very simple code: 1=A, 2=B, 3=C, and so on.

Until this point, there was nothing really out of the ordinary: excellent training, without any doubt, but the idea that a horse might be trained to tap out a certain number of strokes on seeing a given concrete figure was not a thing to get the rationalists up in arms. Only the number of lessons required to learn the alphabet might be something to surprise us.

But Hans did not stop at this point. Having learned his figures, he now learned how to figure. His master wrote 35 + 15 on the board, and Hans tapped out 50.

This time it had definitely gone beyond the limit, and, while there were those who started talking about a miracle, others did not hide their disbelief. The Emperor himself took an interest in the question, and on his orders a commission of professors was appointed to study this wonderful animal's exploits.

The commission filed its report. No doubt about it: the animal acted, not as a result of calculations, but under the guidance of signals that people could not make out, which the trainer's assistants gave when he was coming close to the correct answer.

Von Osten, discouraged as a result, sold the horse to one of his admirers, a very rich man named Krall, who by profession was a jeweler. The latter, convinced of the intelligence of his newly acquired horse, undertook to continue his education and also so to educate two other horses, named Muhamed and Zarif.

Krall set himself to proving the veracity of von Osten's experiments. Among other things, he repeated the most spectacular experiments in complete darkness. Hans and his two fellow students, once having been given the problem, had no trouble in solving it despite the lack of light.

The two new prodigies made fantastic progress; with a maximum of only two hours of lessons a day, they were able in less than two weeks to do addition and subtraction. A few days later, they started in on multiplication and division. After four months of schooling, these wonder pupils were ready for square root and learning the alphabet at the same time.

Krall now added to his team a fourth member, named Hänschen, who showed himself quickly to be just as gifted as his forerunners.

Word of the new accomplishments of the Elberfeld horses (they became famous under the name of the city where their master lived) this time spread to all of Europe and brought about very lively controversies. On the credit side for the period, we should note that estimable scientists and university professors were not averse to making the trip to Elberfeld to see things firsthand. In their minds, there could be no question of the horses really being able to calculate, yet many of them did not want to reject the phenomenon out of hand without having fairly inspected it.

It is not at all certain that such an attitude would prevail in our own day; the specialists consulted would first of all have denounced it all as a fake, whereas, as we shall see, there was something else to it.

Among these more or less sceptical but generally sincere investigators, there was a famous Swiss psychologist named Claparède who has left a very detailed account of his observations.

First of all, he tells us, Krall put on the blackboard a rather complicated problem: the square root of 36 times the square root of 49 equals ? The most gifted of the four horses, Muhamed, was then brought before the blackboard, and he started to tap his foot. First he gave the wrong answer: 52. Then, having been reprimanded by his master, he gave the right one: 42.

The psychologist then suggested a notably more complicated question: what is the square root of the square root of 614,656?

Muhamed tapped twice with his right foot and eight times with the left, giving the correct answer of 28.

Claparède watched several more similar experiments, and went away feeling very much puzzled. In writing his report, he analyzed the different explanations which might be considered.

They were the following: fraud, involuntary signs given by the audience, telepathy, or the existence of intellectual capabilities in animals.

The first explanation was quickly dropped. Krall's good faith could certainly not be questioned. This was a man who believed heart and soul in the intelligence of his animals, and he could not be suspected. Besides, fraud is always fairly easy to detect when it is there.

Fraud, of course, has been very widely used in relation to animal calculators, and it may not be without interest to see how it was gotten away with. The horse is left for a time without food and then is brought to the place where the exhibition will later be held. A helper dangles the oats before the horse's nostrils, while the trainer keeps him from going forward. In his impatience, the horse then starts to paw the ground. At this point the trainer releases him and lets him feed. Soon, the animal acquires the habit of pawing the ground as soon as he is in the exhibition hall and the trainer stands alongside him in a certain way.

From then on, it is easy to command the horse to stop his pawing by a simple signal followed by his oat ration, and this signal may be made virtually imperceptible to the uninitiated. Very quickly, a conditioned reaction sets in, and, the day of the show, the trainer simply gives the signal to stop pawing when the correct number is reached. The desired goal has been achieved; a mathematical horse has been created.

But in the case of the Elberfeld horses, this was not the explanation. Apart from the fact that Krall's personality leads us to eliminate such a possibility, Claparède's intensive investigation and those of many others are there to convince us. Moreover, an act in which the animal taps out the tens with one foot and the digits with the other seems much more difficult to fake.

⟊ TELEPATHY?

For personal reasons, Claparède formally ruled out telepathy, not that he had proved that it was not a possibility. He just simply did not believe in telepathy. For the same reason, he completely eliminated the possibility that the horse might really be able to figure, and he therefore finally had to plump for the idea of involuntary signals given by the audience, signals which might lead the horse to stop tapping once he got close to the right number.

Claparède made one interesting observation. He studied the percentage of correct answers, for Krall's horses were far from infallible, and actually made a great many mistakes.

He recorded 11 per cent correct answers for easy questions and 13 per cent for difficult ones; in another set, there were 7½ per cent right for the easy ones and again 13 per cent for the difficult.

To him, the study of these figures in itself was enough to give the key to the mystery. If the animals had really calculated, they would obviously have done better with the easy problems than with the more difficult ones. But if on the contrary we accept the idea that it was involuntary signals from the audience, it is easy to understand that the latter's tensions were greater for the more difficult questions, and therefore their emotional reactions easier for the horse to apprehend.

A French psychologist, Piéron, maintained that there would be changes in the spectators' breathing rhythms, which would be perceptible to the animal, horses' hearing being particularly acute. Krall, who had already allowed many investigations and subjected himself to all kinds of demands, at this point had all he could take, and Piéron was never able to check on whether his contention could be substantiated.

COUNTER-INVESTIGATION

The matter did not remain there, for other investigators had other ideas and, luckier than Piéron, were allowed to check them out.

Maeterlinck visited Krall's horses, and it seems they made a deep impression on the mind of the writer who so often tried to fathom the mysteries of animal life.

Krall began by repeating the writer's name several times to Muhamed and then asked the horse to say it. The animal did not hesitate but tapped out in code Mazrik which, it must be admitted, can be accepted as a fairly good approximation of the difficult spelling. The poet was allowed to stay alone with the horse and set a number of problems to him, to which he immediately got the answers, answers he was not himself aware of at the moment.

Professors Mackensie and Assagioli were given permission to work with the youngest of the horses, Hänschen, without the presence of Krall or his handlers.

The two professors would write problems on the blackboard and get correct answers a very satisfying percentage of the time.

After that, they put the horse in a room alone and, after having written a problem on the board, went out. Observations then took place through a peephole, and still the answers continued to amaze the observers.

A German, Professor Hartkopf—well-named in this case, since in German that means "hard head"—refused to be impressed with these results and wanted to make sure the horse could not get guidance by watching the experimenter in the peephole. He had the questions prepared by third parties, then took them out of their envelopes. Without himself knowing the answers to the questions, Hartkopf allowed the horse to answer and only then opened the other envelope containing the right answer.

The horse took only a few seconds to give the answer, and in this short time, Hartkopf, who himself was no lightning calculator, was not able to work out the answer for himself. The questions involved were anything but simple: they called, for example, for the cube root of 29,791 or of 103,823. Then, the experimenters pushed the animal on to the fourth root of various six-digit numbers, and when we know that the root of 456,776 was given correctly in approximately ten seconds, we realize how improbable the theory of involuntary signals given by the audience becomes.

As a result of the fame of the Elberfeld horses, a veritable epidemic [1] of horse and dog calculators occurred in Germany. If it proved impossible to train an elephant for this, dogs turned out to be especially brilliant, and those of Frau Moeckel, of Mannheim, became almost as famous as Krall's horses.

There was Rolf, a terrier whose talent was discovered by chance one day when his mistress was giving an arithmetic lesson to her

[1] American rivals of the German horses should be mentioned. Among them, especially noteworthy was Lady, a mare who answered questions after first having gone into a trance. She was not only gifted at figures, but was adept at languages, too, and is said to have answered easily questions put to her in Chinese!

There is also the case of Black Bear, a pony with a special aptitude for geometry.

daughters, who were failing miserably; Rolf started to give the answers in their place by striking the table with his paw.

Naturally, among all these tales, there were a large number of shaggy dogs, and it is just as well, in the final analysis, to be satisfied with the Elberfeld horses for the discussion of this strange question.

⌄ THE MYSTERY REMAINS

The theory of involuntary signals persisted for a long time. Yet, as we saw, Hartkopf dealt it a fatal blow, and it should really no longer be countenanced. Still, whenever anyone brings this question up, in 95 per cent of the cases that is the theory advanced to explain away the facts!

If we reject it, what, then, will we accept?

It seems absolutely ridiculous to believe that horses with their mental power are able to solve problems of this sort. Must we then stand mute? This is probably the wisest attitude one can take, but it is still permissible to recall that there are other inexplicable phenomena in the world. Lavondes, in a book about horses, quotes the opinion of those who claim that the blows struck by the horse's hoofs, like the tapping of spirit tables, are translating processes going on in the unconscious of those who question them.

All other things being equal, it is possible, by way of tentative conclusion, to quote the ideas set out by Aimé Michel in a recent work on the subject. "What is involved is not animal calculation, but some unknown interaction between human and animal thought. Everything took place at Elberfeld as if human thought were able, under certain circumstances difficult to elucidate, to have a direct effect upon the animal. Should this be traced back to hypnotism? Or to thought transmission? To psi effects? We will never know this finally unless we resume the old experiments in a new way."

γ

Will We Talk with Animals?

γ

IN May 1959, there was founded in the United States a non-profit association, called the inter-species Communications Research Institute. Among the founder-members was Dr. John C. Lilly, whose laboratory was to be sole headquarters for the said Institute.

The Institute's purpose was the study of inter-species communications, which could only mean animals, for we know of no other form of life which has a sufficiently developed psychic life.

Before looking into Dr. Lilly's works, it is not without interest to ask ourselves some questions: is there an animal language, and can we understand it? Can animals understand our language?

Let us try to answer the latter of these questions, easier to handle than the former.

γ CAN ANIMALS UNDERSTAND HUMANS?

Any hunting dog understands a few orders, and some specially trained dogs can obey a rather large number of very varied orders; all domestic animals share this to an extent. Elephants in India understand no less than twenty different commands. This contention of elephant drivers was checked out by a physiologist from Munster University while on a trip to India. And this is no record, nor anything out of the ordinary.

Miss Farff, an Englishwoman who raised the most diverse kinds of animals and had a great way with wild beasts, succeeded in teaching a seal the meanings of 35 words. Her two otters respectively understood 18 and 16 words; a rat was able to learn six words and her two squirrels five words each. Naturally, these are all words that have a direct meaning for the animal and are generally connected with a specific action.

Thus, the seal could understand inside, outside, boat, swim, ball, and also (since this was a musical seal) words like trumpet and harmonica. The rat understood its name and five other words: basket, outside, grapes, nuts, and roof.

The squirrels were less advanced, and could not tell "nuts" from "grapes," both words simply meaning "food" to them.

With teaching, a chimpanzee, it seems, can succeed in mastering without too much difficulty as many as sixty-odd words.

The human voice has a very strange effect on wild animals. Tamers and trainers are well aware of this and often talk continuously to their animals. Hunters know this, too, and the clans which specialize in hunting lions or crocodiles or other wild beasts jealously guard the words and rhythms which are effective when they find themselves face to face with their adversary. According to many specialists, such incantations not only have a pacifying effect on the human but also very visibly affect the behavior of the animal, who seems less bent on attacking.

Therefore, the question is settled: there can be, in the mind of an animal, a certain association between human language on the one hand and objects or actions on the other.

ʳ A N I M A L S   T H A T   S P E A K   O U R   L A N G U A G E

Another aspect of the question is the animals' ability to imitate human talk.

As far as simians are concerned, we have very little positive information. Teaching one to talk is a very discouraging task, and we know only of Furness who had patience enough to persevere until he actually achieved some results. He spent no less than five years trying to teach a chimpanzee the one word "momma," and at that the word was hissed more than spoken and was difficult for outsiders to understand.

He had more luck with the orang-utang. With infinite patience, several times a day, Furness would stay before a mirror, holding the orang-utang's head alongside his own so that the animal could see his own lip movements at the same time as those of his master.

With his hand, Furness would move the animal's lips, forcing him to make sounds. It took him only six months to teach this pupil to say "papa." After that, he taught him to say "cup," but that was the end of the experiment, for the animal died shortly afterwards. It must be pointed out that the orang-utang did not repeat these words mechanically but used both of them in a manner perfectly suited to their meanings. He called his master "papa" when he saw him and said "cup" only when he was asking for a drink.

A few years ago, the short chapter on the use of words by mammals ended right there. Now, it is not possible to overlook the research done by Dr. Lilly.[1]

He began his study of dolphins [2] on St. Thomas in the Virgin Islands. Why did he choose this relatively difficult animal? The an-

---

[1] Dr. Lilly had a famous forerunner, Dr. Garner, also an American. In one of Jules Verne's lesser-known novels, *The Great Forest,* there are juicy details about this precursor. Jules Verne, who closely followed the scientific concerns of his time, created in that book the character of Dr. Johansen, who followed in Garner's footsteps and did much better than he.

Professor Garner was interested only in monkeys, but he wrote: "My knowledge of the animal world has given me the firm belief that all mammals are capable of speaking to a degree proportionate to their experience."

In 1892, Garner left America for Gabon, where he lived in Libreville until 1894. At that time, he decided to go upcountry, where he was given shelter at a mission of the Fathers of the Holy Ghost located on the banks of the Ogowe.

If we are to believe the scientist, he spent three months living in a cage, deep in the forest, and was able to study the gorilla in its native habitat. But according to Jules Verne, who seems to have been well-informed, Garner spent only three nights in his cage: "Devoured by myriads of mosquitoes, he could not stand it any longer, took the cage down, and returned to ask hospitality of the Fathers of the Holy Ghost, who gave it to him without remuneration. Finally, June 18th, giving up his expedition for good, he went back to England, and thence to America, bringing back as the only souvenirs of his trip two little chimpanzees which resolutely refused to speak to him."

This did not keep Garner from publishing works on ape language, which according to him consisted principally of nine sounds, modified by some thirty modulations. He even furnished an embryo glossary in which we learn that "whoo" means food, "cheny" drink, and "iegk" watch out.

[2] The first dolphin trained in the present period for scientific purposes was called Flippy. He was caught in 1947 and put into an aquarium on the Florida coast.

The first dolphin trainer was named Frohn. A German by birth, he had specialized in training seals and otaries.

Since then, a large number of trained dolphins have been performing in the great marine circuses set up on the Atlantic and Pacific coasts of the United States.

swer is to be found in manuals of comparative anatomy; while the human brain averages about two and three-quarter pounds in weight in a person five feet nine inches tall, that of *tursiops truncatus,* one of the most common of the dolphins, reaches over three and three-quarter pounds for a size of eight feet or so. If we compare these figures with those for monkeys and prehominidae, we cannot fail to be impressed. A chimpanzee brain weighs only about three-quarters of a pound and that of a gorilla just about a pound. Australopithecus probably had no more than the chimpanzee's three-quarters of a pound, pithecanthropus about a pound and one-half, and sinanthropus about two pounds.

Lilly is of the opinion that, if it exists, the language indigenous to the species can produce the same effects as human talk for men.

But a dolphin placed in absolute solitude, in a condition of "acoustical deprivation," will learn to enjoy the only language that he hears, that of his keepers. Every time the dolphin vocalized or whistled, Lilly played for the animal a recording of a human voice counting from one to five. It appeared that the captive dolphin appreciated what he was given to listen to and increased the amount of his own chatterings so as to earn the reward more often.

After that, the dolphin was allowed to listen all day long to the conversation of his keepers, through a loudspeaker connected to a live microphone. At the same time, a hydrophone placed in the aquarium with its speaker in the laboratory allowed the researchers to follow the animal's vocalizing. It is most striking to note that there appeared very quickly attempts to imitate human language—attempts which at first were very rough, a fact which, when one knows the differences between the dolphin's vocal organ and ours, is in no way surprising. The sounds this animal can make, always very sharp, belong to some extent to the ultrasonic area outside our hearing range.

Despite this handicap, the dolphin imitates man. Lilly has classified these imitations into four categories:

1. Imitation of human laughter. This is a series of "hah-hah-hahs," sounding like a child's laugh and often to be heard a few seconds after a woman has laughed.

2. Whistling. This sound is natural to the dolphin, but it seems

that the animal often tries to imitate the whistling of a human voice or of some electrical equipment.

3. Various imitations. Noises made by pressing the lips against the palm of one's hand or other more or less incongruous sounds are often imitated by dolphins with quite a bit of realism.

4. Imitation of human words. This is the most interesting and most extraordinary contribution of Lilly's work. He asserts he has heard and recorded dolphins repeating words in a very high range. Let us quote him directly: "I have heard most distinctly the following words and phrases 'copied' in an extremely high-pitched and brief fashion: 'three-two-three,' 'Tee ar Pee' (the letters 'TRR' were just given), and a host of others, less clear but verging so closely on humanlike rhythm, enunciation, and phonetic quality as to be eerie."

Lilly also tells a scarcely believable story.

On April 16, 1960, one of the dolphins, named Lizzie, seemed to be very ill: Lilly and his crew were trying to take care of her when, over the loudspeaker, came the voice of someone calling the researchers to tell them they would miss dinner if they did not come right away.

"It's six o'clock," it said.

Lilly answered the call and never again saw Lizzie, who died during the night.

Later, listening to the tape recorded in the aquarium that day, Lilly heard that urgent "It's six o'clock," and almost immediately afterward a series of whistles and a sentence in an almost human voice. The sentence could have been merely a bad imitation of "It's six o'clock," but Lilly and the rest of the people listening to the tape thought it sounded more like, "This is a trick," very clearly said, even if in more of a hiss than a statement.

Was it coincidence? An illusion?

At any rate, the inter-species Communications Research Institute is just at its beginning. The Institute will doubtless have many duplicates, for the scientific world is more and more interested in dolphins, and it will not be long before we know whether Lilly's anticipations are based merely on excessive optimism or on extraordinary secrets.

But dolphins, in the field of language, are far behind birds, many species of which are most gifted in reproducing the human voice. The best-known are parrots, and, among the stories about these animals, it is especially interesting to select those which denote not just an imitation but an intelligent application of a word or a sentence.

In their natural state, parrots never imitate the human voice. All imitative birds are more or less social animals which normally live in bands. Once in captivity, they feel their isolation and switch their overrunning affection to the living beings they see most often—humans.

A parrot accustomed to living among humans tries to communicate by imitating the sounds made by his new companions just as in the wilds he had communicated with those of his own species. It is striking, moreover, that parrots tend to talk most volubly when their masters have just left them.

Among the famous parrots we should mention Jaco, who belonged to the species known as the African gray. This bird lived in Salzburg from 1827 to 1854 and was the delight of a good part of the city for all that time. Many tales related by the famous naturalist Brehm give us quite a precise idea of what he was capable of.

Jaco was especially observant about everything that went on in his little world. He greeted visitors with a "Good day" in the morning and a "Good afternoon" in the afternoon. When his master came in, he would call, "Papa, come here." When someone knocked at the door, he called out in a masculine voice, "Come in! I'm at your service," or "How good to see you," or else, "I'm pleased to greet you." When the cathedral bell rang out, he answered, "I'm coming! God be with you! I'm coming." When his master went out, the parrot never failed to say, "God be with you," and if the master was not alone he would change it to "God be with you all." Jaco's owner acquired a partridge, and when it sang for the first time, Jaco turned toward the bird and commented, "Bravo, little one, bravo!"

But Jaco, for all his accomplishments, seems quite ordinary by comparison with one of his congeners called Coco. This one spoke very good Dutch, French, and German. His vocabulary was quite extensive and very well adapted. If he wanted to drink or eat, he would yelp, "Coco wants wah-wah, Coco wants to eat," and if he was not given satisfaction immediately: "Coco wants to and must eat now." He liked to joke and could be quite funny. An old major whom he had known for a long time tried to teach him some tricks:

"Get up on the perch, Coco, up ,on the perch," he commanded. The parrot remained speechless for a moment at this demand, then burst into laughter, and commanded in turn: "Major, up on the perch, come on, major!" "He was practically human," was what those who knew him wrote about this animal, and the stories about him are legion.

We will quote just one more, particularly amusing. George, the son of the household, once came home late at night after a rather long absence and, having greeted his parents, wanted to see Coco. He lifted the curtain which covered the cage and was taken aback by the considerate voice which softly said to him, "Ah, you're back now, George. Well, that's good, yes, very good."

Colonel von Lukanus, a very well-known ornithologist, also had a gray parrot which has remained very famous. This bird lived in the company of a hoopoe which it called "Höpfchen." Hoopoes do not live long in captivity, and Höpfchen was no exception to the rule.

Nine years after the hoopoe died, the colonel chanced to get another one, and when the parrot saw it for the first time, it immediately cried out, "Höpfchen, Höpfchen!"

There are other cases of extraordinary parrots.

Professor Köhler, who only a short time ago held the chair of zoology at the University of Freiburg-in-Bresgau, had one of these birds. The animal was extremely polite and on the departure of each visitor would say, *"Na, auf Wiedersehen,"* in a low and particularly warm voice. That in itself would not be extraordinary, but what was more surprising was that he never uttered the sentence at the wrong time.

Once in a while, a visitor would go toward the door, put his hand on the knob, and look like he was leaving, enough to fool anyone—except the professor's parrot, who never said his good-bye until the visitor actually made up his mind to leave.

This astonishing animal intuition is another form of language which could warrant further study. Along these lines, there is a story that is told by Lorenz. It is about a bitch that the famous naturalist owned in the early years of his professional career.

This companion spent long hours in her master's study, curled up under the desk, patiently waiting for the walk which ended the day. But first Lorenz had to keep his appointments; if the visitor was nice, nothing happened; but if, on the other hand, the visitor gave her master a hard time, the dog would rouse herself from her torpor, grab hold of the objectionable one's pants leg, and start pulling him toward the door. How, from her spot under the desk, she could tell how well her master and his visitor were getting along—this is a question which is unanswered, and which takes its place in the long list of similar ones.

But let us get back to talking birds. After parrots, the most gifted (and some hold that they are even better) are the mynah birds.

Pierre Pellerin has a very good story about three mynahs living in a pet shop in three different cages.

These birds were particularly loud-mouthed. While one of them imitated the sound of dishes being smashed, the second would yell, "Cut it out, now, shut your trap!" and the third would chime in, "You, too, banana-head!" The time came when this extraordinary trio had to be split up. The mynah which had been sold was carried out through the pet shop door, without any hope of coming back. To the amazement of all concerned, before disappearing, he turned back and, with a last look at the pet shop saleswoman and his play-mates, called out: "Good-bye, mother, good-bye, old pals!"

Although they are not of the same morphological structure as man's, the mynah's phonetic organs can emit true vowels. This implies the presence of three distinct soundboxes, corresponding to our own pharynxes, mouths, and noses.

A number of other birds, on the other hand, would seem to have only two soundboxes at their disposal.

⸌ TRUE ANIMAL LANGUAGE

Comprehension and use of human talk are of interest to us, without doubt, but is there a language of the animals themselves? There are certainly examples of transmission of information relating to a current condition, particularly some emotion or some physiological phenomenon. Among the classic examples, it is worth mentioning the social code of the wolves which was studied by Schnekel at the Basel Zoo.

We have already dealt with the question of pecking order. Bands of wolves are no exception to this rule, and among them, as in other social organizations, transgressions of the established rules are cause for fights. They do not require much of a pretext: let an inferior dare to eat or drink before one of his betters, and immediately the fight is on.

Under such conditions, we can readily understand the need for some kind of regulating mechanism. In particular, each animal must be informed about the hierarchical rank and the intentions of his congeners. Wolves express their rank and their mood through a complicated code which involves movements of the tail and the ears as well as making faces.

There are many other examples of communication between animals, whether for the transmission of information among members of one society or because individual animals living alone nevertheless feel a need to proclaim the state of their souls for the benefit of their neighbors.

For instance, a male chaffinch, through his song, can impart the following information to those concerned: "I am a male; I am on my own territory; I see an enemy in the sky, on the ground, etc."

Wild geese give us a good example of the exchange of information within a social group. These birds move about in coordinated formations. Flights of wild geese in the sky have the geometric characteristics of well-trained air squadrons. Our domestic geese do the same when going out into the fields. This coordination of movement is achieved through a pseudolanguage which Lorenz has carefully studied. When a goose is thoroughly satisfied that it has located an abundant food supply in a good safe place, it starts a particular kind of clucking made up of a large number of syllables. Other members of the group, if they are in the same frame of mind, answer similarly. But if a goose feels a sudden urge to move away, it makes a slightly different clucking. The number of syllables is very sharply reduced and, if a majority of the geese cluck the same way, the whole group takes off in a body.

The smaller the number of syllables, the greater the need to leave in a hurry; using only two or three syllables means there is little time to waste. A monosyllabic honk is the alarm signal to which the whole school responds by immediate flight for life. There is only one exception to this rule: mother geese, in charge of goslings, stay on the ground to protect the young.

While these examples may seem surprising, they are still only transmissions of information about a present state of the animal. We know of only one example that deals with a fact that took place in the past, and this example involves the bee.

These social-living insects have worked out a code which allows a better exploitation of the natural resources needed for the good of the colony. When an exploring bee has discovered a field of flowers, it comes back to the hive and informs the workers about its discovery.

If the source of the food is in the immediate neighborhood of the hive, the explorer does a circular dance on the comb, within a diameter scarcely greater than the length of its body. Collectors not at the moment assigned to any other work come to watch this dance and comprehend very well what the explorer is saying: "Within a bare 100 yards of the hive, there is a source of food which has the aroma of the nectar I am now distributing to you." Once in possession of this information the collectors fly off and undertake the exploitation of the mine described.

Things are different, however, when the flowers are further away. It is obviously rather easy to spot within a range of 100 yards or so flowers whose aroma has already been made familiar. But locating them within a radius of a mile or more can involve a considerable waste of time and of energy.

Two pieces of information, therefore, become indispensable: the distance and the direction. Bees have "understood" this very well, and the discoverer gives them these two indications with the greatest possible detail.

The dance in a circle is then replaced by a dance in a figure eight, or more precisely in the shape of a circle crossed by a bar. While following this line, the dancer shakes her abdomen with a very Oriental belly-dancer-type shimmy, which has naturally led the dance to be designated as a "shimmy."

The distance is very simply indicated by frequency of the shimmies. That is, the quicker the dancer's wiggles the closer the source of the food.

Direction is indicated in a more complicated manner. The basic datum that has to be given is the angle formed by the position of the sun and that of the location of the food. The dancer translates this angle into one of equal value made between the bar of the eight, the shimmying line, and the direction of gravity.

The information is completed by the aroma of the nectar the dancer supplies.

Bees have been experimentally confronted with an especially difficult problem. A source of food is put on the other side of an impassable barrier, such as a rocky spur. The bees to whom this provender is offered have to make a detour in order to get back to the hive.

Once they are back home, they start to dance and indicate the direction of the food without making any mention of the barrier. However, the distance described does take into account the detour that has to be made on the way.

The greatest distance ever indicated by a dancing bee is about seven miles. This extreme was observed by von Frisch during an experiment which was made in the Tyrol. Taking advantage of a famine period, it was possible to train the bees to come gather their food at an artificial source of nectar. By gradually moving this source further away, the collectors were finally lured to very great distances away from the hive. Under normal conditions, the radius of action for the workers does not exceed two miles.

Different races of domestic bees do not appear to speak the same dialect. Italian bees and black bees seem to have some difficulty in understanding each other. And the differences are much greater among the three other known species, which live in Southeast Asia.

One is hard put to decide which is to be the more admired, the insect which has worked out so complex a communications system, or the zoologist who succeeded in deciphering it. The credit for that goes to the famous Austrian entomologist von Frisch, who devoted his entire life to the study of this extra-human language. We cannot sum up in a few pages the work done by a man and his students over a period of more than thirty years, but we will list a few of their discoveries.

Bees are able to tell the position of the sun even when the skies are more or less overcast. They get this information either from a slant of the polarization of light coming through little patches of blue sky (they can gauge this slant) or from the ultraviolet rays which cut through certain layers of clouds. The description of distance they give, however, is only relative.

For instance, if the trip was made against the wind or by rising to a certain altitude, the distance computed on return to the hive will be greater than that actually covered; the indications they give therefore relate to flying time or energy required for the flight rather than to distance in yardage, but this is clearly information being given about something which is already past.

This language is not used only in connection with food gathering; it is used also at the time of swarming. Explorers leave the swarm waiting up in a tree while seeking a suitable location for a new colony. In such a case, one can often see several explorers dancing around the surface of the swarm, each indicating a different location.

One of von Frisch's students, Professor Lindauer, wondered how agreement was reached between the thousands of workers, for the swarm, at a given moment, flies off and heads in a body directly for the one location selected. It would seem that the explorers must express value judgments on their respective discoveries in terms of certain criteria: elevation from the ground, types of walls, size, exposure, etc. Those which discover the best sites seem to dance with the greatest energy. Little by little the different dancers give up their presentations from lack of conviction, and the only one left is the one which discovered the ideal hiving place. These dances can go on for hours when several comparably interesting sites are competing with each other.

✓ ON THE THRESHOLD OF NUMERATION

This sense of symbol, these pre-languages, can be found in many aspects of animal psychism.

We have already spoken about animal calculators. Let us put the question frankly: can animals count?

This question finds its answer in many day-to-day situations. There is a well-known story of four hunters who lie in wait in a cabin for a nearby group of crows. Three of them leave, under the watchful eye of the crows who are not fooled by this and still will not reveal themselves. They are obviously able to tell the difference between three men and four. On the other hand we know they are unable to differentiate nine men from ten.

But such observations cannot replace experiment, and in this area we are especially well off, for Professor Köhler has made very profitable incursions into it.

As far as counting is concerned, he often experimented with pigeons to try to determine their potential.

One way is to offer one of them a cardboard platter on which two lines of seeds have been laid out, two in one line, three in the other. The group of two is sometimes on the left, sometimes on the right, without any specific pattern. The bird is allowed to eat the seeds in one line, either the two or the three, but is forbidden, by a movement of the hand, to get near the seeds in the other group.

Very quickly the pigeon catches on and no longer tries to get at the food in the other line—which proves that the pigeon is able to tell the difference between two and three. But this bird is not really very gifted, for while it is able to distinguish three from four, and four from five, when confronted with five and six it cannot tell the difference.

Other birds can do much better. Jackdaws and parakeets can tell five from six. Parrots, crows, and squirrels succeed in telling six from seven. A child and a rhesus monkey can tell 17 from 18, but adult man is not very good on this score.

Köhler had over 200 adult human subjects look at a screen on which were shown groups of dots for the same period of time as that taken by the animals to make their selections. None of them went beyond telling six from seven, and some of them did only as well as the pigeon.

Adult man, in learning to count with the help of numeral adjectives, no doubt partly loses the ability for unformulated numbering and can then just barely equal the accomplishment of animals considered to be on a lower level.

Other, much more complicated, experiments carried the work even further in this area.

Köhler tried offering a pigeon peas which were sent along a tube and allowed to drop in a ladle. The bird was allowed to eat them all—except No. 6, No. 12, and so on. The peas did not drop at regular intervals, the times varying from one to six seconds between peas. Yet, the pigeon very quickly learned to recognize which pea was not for him.

Birds can also be taught to handle much more complex situations. Some of them can effect transpositions. A crow had been taught that he was allowed to lift a lid on which there were three spots, but that any lids that had two spots or four spots were tabu. One day, he was confronted with lids which did not have spots on them but had flour worms, a delicacy he is very fond of. Instead of lifting the lids to get at the food underneath, the crow devoured the worms from the lids on which there were three, while not touching those worms which were two or four to a lid.

Some transposition experiments that have been carried out are absolutely unbelievable. Logler succeeded in training a gray parrot to eat only two seeds after he had been shown two light flashes, and three seeds after three flashes. Later on, the light flashes are replaced by sounds—whistles, bells, drumbeats—and in each case the bird showed his reaction to the number and not the character of the stimuli by eating only the corresponding number of seeds. It was possible in this way to obtain coordination with as many as fifteen different kinds of stimuli, which seems quite remarkable.

⟨ CAN MAN SPEAK ANIMAL LANGUAGE?

There is still a fourth aspect of this question of animals and language which we have to consider: can man use animal language?

To communicate with an animal, would it not be better to try to speak his language to him, rather than trying to make him learn ours? Would Lilly not have been better off if he had tried to "learn dolphin"?

On this score, any hunter who has ever tried to imitate bird- or animal-calls with the strange gadgets made for this purpose knows very well that there is no point in making just any old sound. There have been many cases where novices have imitated a bird-call perfectly—except that it was the birds' alarm signal—and the game they were trying to attract took off on the double.

Zoopsychologists have gone much deeper into this than hunters. Konrad Lorenz has succeeded in communicating with geese and in giving them orders. By making the proper clucking sounds and waving his arms, by running or by suddenly lying down on the ground, he has been able to direct a flock of geese, to get it to fly away, and then to land.

Szymanski's experiment is much stranger still, for he succeeded in entering into communication with snails. These mollusks, although they are hermaphrodites, do mate with each other after an interminable series of ceremonies. Their love messages are delivered through a thin calcareous needle which each individual delicately deploys to give his partner tactile stimulations, the exact character of which we can have no idea of. Nevertheless, Szymanski, after long and patient observations, did succeed in paying court to a snail and in getting it to make the anticipated responses.

As for the language of the bees, Stech put it to use, too, by means of a dead bee manipulated as a decoy outside the hive; he is entitled to the distinction of being the first human being to have entered into contact with the insect world.

These various examples are of course of differing degrees of value. Geese are not so far removed from us; in the case of the snail, we cannot truthfully say it is a language; and as far as the bee is concerned, the first attempts have been only of the very roughest kind.

The fact remains that it is possible to communicate with the animal world and that each day the temptation to do so grows in importance. Man, just beginning to look up into the skies and not knowing what awaits him there, should not overlook this chance to become more familiar with the non-human.

✓

Conclusion

✓

THE study of animal psychic life, of what one might call inhuman psychism, brings us to a rather paradoxical conclusion.

On the one hand, there is no doubt of our own relationship to the animal: too many analogies, too many convergences force us to recognize it. On the other hand, the totally alien aspect of that world is no less evident.

For it is quite certain that each species, because of its sense potential and its own interests, lives in a personal universe in which systems of reference can be totally different. Von Uexküll found it amusing to color several drawings of the inside of an apartment by giving a conventional color to each object in it in function of the meaning it would have respectively for a man, a dog, or a tame jackdaw. This brought out sharply some obvious things which at first glance might seem a little naïve. A chair, for instance, signifies nothing to a jackdaw, which finds its favorite resting place on a hanging perch. But there is still no better way to underline the striking differences which exist between two living beings than in their manner of apprehending the universe.

Later on, the objectivists reinforced this notion. They showed to what extent the significance of a specific object could vary, not only from species to species, but also according to the circumstances. Let us remember the philanthid which at certain phases of its hunt places a value on a dead bee, but in other phases has no idea of what it is. This idea of meaningful stimulus, which plays its part at very definite moments of behavior, is no doubt one of the most extraordinary discoveries about animal psychology.

⚹ TOWARD A PSYCHOLOGY OF THE NON-HUMAN

This idea alone allows us to undertake the study of any inhuman psychic action. It is also a very dependable guarantee against indulging in anthropomorphism since, in the innumerable experiments cited, the researcher leaves the decisions to the animal. The psychologist restricts himself to varying the conditions of the stimulus, while the animal dictates the results by acting or not acting.

Of course, there is always the serious problem of bringing about the stimulus correctly. One can act only upon what he is able to conceive. Very quickly, when the opposite is true, the limitations of the procedure become apparent. For instance, it is of no use to know that the sense potential of such and such a living being has nothing in common with our own if the physical phenomena to be taken into account are totally unknown to us. Our ideas about the attraction that flowers can have for insects, or the experiments of researchers in this field, ran into an impassable wall as long as we were not aware of ultraviolet rays and what the colors represented exactly on the physical plane.

In the same way, as long as we continue to explain the inexplicable by talking about "telepathic" phenomena, we will go around in circles. This will stop only when, having understood the essentials of the suspected mechanisms, we can make them into a valid explanation.

As things stand today, it is no more helpful to maintain that the pigeon gets back to its master through some telepathic process than to say, as was done in the nineteenth century, that bees are strongly attracted by the red color of the poppy, since we now know the bee does not see that color at all, but is attracted by ultraviolet. This all amounts to saying that we should not allow ourselves to be lulled to sleep by the "fascinating virtues of opium" and that purely verbal intellectual satisfactions must be pitilessly rejected. On the other hand, we can rejoice when we succeed in making a phenomenon reproducible and are able to predict the reactions of an organism. Even if the basic theory is still missing, that much at least is an indication of progress in the direction of discovery.

But above all we must give up the preconceived idea that nothing can exist in the world which is radically different from our own psyche. Man is so made that he would reject anything which seems to him to reduce his dignity. That the earth is not the navel of the universe, that man is physically related to the animals, that a subconscious sometimes imposes its law on our conscious ego—these are ideas which have met with and still meet with a good deal of opposition.

Assert now that different types of psychic action may have come into being in such or such branch of animal evolution, that psychisms exist with which we find no grounds of comparison, and we all rebel. On the other hand, we accept the study of infrahuman levels easily. The monkey is almost a man, the rat is a forerunner of man, the frog in his behavior sometimes suggests our own at an elementary level—these are assertions which gain universal acceptance.

It is possible to draw beautiful growth charts covering psychic levels and correlating these with the development of the organs of the nervous system. Man then can see that he is superior to another psyche of the same type as his own and, if from time to time these animals accomplish things of which we are not capable, this in no way bothers us; it does not even make us feel we have been caught short.

We feel differently when dealing with other groups which are more alien to us. Octopuses, insects, spiders are not only far from us by the structure of their bodies, but also by their psyches. To try to apply our criteria to them is an aberration.

Naturally, if we consider nothing but the level of their accomplishments, their psychic development can be considered to be inferior—even though one might really wonder what a mammal would be doing with a brain that had the same number of neurons as an ant's. But even if we recognize a kind of inferiority in certain species, we still cannot deny their originality.

What science-fiction writer will paint a proper picture of an insect society as compared to ours? On one side, our individual efforts to accumulate knowledge; on the other, innate knowledge. On the one side, considerable variations of level among members of society in the handling of this knowledge, and on the other apparently the most absolute equality. We could go on and on that way. . .

The great argument for our superiority is no doubt the lightning speed with which the human species has progressed, while insects have apparently remained stagnant. But this is not absolutely true: the bee started out as a lone animal quite incapable of building geometric constructions or communicating information to its congeners.

But let us stop the game right here. For, as you have understood, this is essentially a matter of playing around with a few ideas and not one of claiming that a bee society or an ant society is superior to ours.

The very fact that we recognize the "different" character of insect societies in itself wipes out the significance of any judgment of superiority or inferiority which we may make. A dark red is no doubt more deeply colored than a pale blue, but it is certainly not bluer and cannot be said to be "more" in every respect. This is the light in which we ought to look at the animal psyche, most especially that of the invertebrates.

To get used to looking at what is foreign to us on a level below our own is, incidentally, perhaps not bad training for that day when we will have to confront other worlds—on our own level, alongside of us, or even above us.

A Dictionary of Those Responsible

A Dictionary of Those Responsible

RENÉ DESCARTES (1596-1650)

In his work, *The Discourse on Method* (1637), he developed the theory of the machine-animal which was to influence succeeding generations to such an extent as to make impossible the appearance of animal psychology at the same time as other branches of biology. The highest accomplishments of the animal psyche are considered in it as merely the workings of a "clock made up only of wheels and springs."

R. A. F. DE RÉAUMUR (1683-1757)

A universal mind, he was interested in all of the sciences. In his *Memoirs to Be Used for the History of Insects,* published from 1734 to 1742, in six volumes, he became the true founder of entomology. His meticulous analysis of instinctive behaviors made him the creator of the ethological method, even though his theoretical views on these questions may be outmoded today.

CHARLES R. DARWIN (1809-1882)

A British naturalist, during a trip around the world aboard the *Beagle,* he became aware of the fact of evolution. His works and thoughts deal not only with anatomy or comparative psychology, but also often the animal psyche. In this connection, *The Descent of Man* (1871) and *The Expression of Emotions in Man and Animals* (1872) constitute master works. The introduction of the idea of evolution into the consideration of animal psychology was naturally a contribution of the greatest value.

SIR JOHN LUBBOCK (1834-1913)

This amateur British entomologist was one of the pioneers of experimental animal psychology. His works on the perception of colors in insects are very much ahead of the tendencies generally prevailing in his day. He is especially remembered for a book about social insects, *Ants, Bees, and Wasps* (1882).

J. H. FABRE (1823-1915)

Amateur French entomologist. A member of the teaching profession until 1871, when he retired to Sérignan to devote himself to the study of insects. From 1879 to 1907, he published ten volumes of *Entomological Memoirs,* which are a condensation of all of the work of this man, who has been called the Homer of insects. He introduced the experimental method into the study of complex instinctive behaviors and applied particularly rigorously the method of direct observation instituted by Réaumur.

HERBERT SPENCER JENNINGS (1868-1947)

This American biologist specialized in the study of the lower forms of life. He was responsible for developing the theory of apprenticeship through trial and error. His basic work, *Behavior of the Lower Organisms* (1906), was republished in 1962 with a new introduction by Donald O. Jensen.

JACQUES LOEB (1859-1924)

A native of Germany, this biologist in 1888 evolved the theory of tropisms. Becoming very controversial early in his university career, he emigrated to California, where he was able to continue his research. One of his master works is the book, *Forced Movements, Tropisms, and Animal Conduct,* published in 1918.

WOLFGANG KÖHLER (1887-   )

A German naturalist, in 1912 he founded a biological station, devoted to the study of chimpanzees, in the Canary Islands. The results obtained were remarkable for that period. They brought out the animal's potential for learning to use tools and its ability to make quite complex "detours" in order to reach a goal. He published, in German, *The Mentality of Apes* (1925).

R. M. YERKES (1876-1956)

An American psychologist, who was especially interested in the psychology of the larger apes. At Orange Park, Florida, in 1930, he founded a specialized laboratory which now bears his name. Among his most significant works: *The Great Apes, a Study of Anthropoid Life* (1929) and *Chimpanzees, a Laboratory Colony* (1943).

I. P. PAVLOV (1849-1936)

Russian physiologist. He won the Nobel Prize in 1904 for his work on digestion, but has remained famous especially for his work on conditioned reflexes which, from 1928 to his death, were his exclusive pursuit. Among his master works, those which deserve particular mention in their English translations are *Conditioned Reflexes* (1927) and *Conditiontd Reflexes and Psychiatry* (1941).

OTTO KÖHLER

Contemporary German ethologist. He taught for many years at the University of Freiburg-in-Bresgau. His experimental research dealt mainly with the counting ability of various animals: parrot, pigeon, squirrel, etc. The main part of his work has appeared in the *Zeitschrift für Tierpsychologie,* of which he is co-editor.

HEINI HEDIGER (1908-)

Swiss ethologist, currently curator of the Zurich Zoo. Known for his studies of psychology in the zoo and in the cirius, as well as for his works on the territories of wild animals. Among his writings, one can cite, *Wild Animals in Captivity* (1950), *Psychology of Animals in the Zoo and the Circus* (1950), and *Observations on Animal Psychology in the National Parks of the Belgian Congo* (1951).

KONRAD LORENZ (1903-)

Austrian ethologist, founder of the school of objective ethology as it exists today. Has published many theoretical writings on animal psychology and numerous reports of observations dealing especially with geese and ducks. Uses a special method, which consists of familiarizing the animal under consideration as completely as possible with the observer, so that the latter may be accepted as a companion by the individual animal or the group. His popular works, which are of the highest calibre, serve as an easy initiation to the thought of this author (e.g., *On Aggression,* New York, 1966).

KARL VON FRISCH (1886-)

Austrian entomologist. Around his chair as professor at the University of Munich, he has created a school devoted to the study of the bee and especially that insect's language. His masterful work has become a classic. In addition, it includes some very interesting contributions on the bee's sensory organs, obtained by very advanced training methods.

G. P. BAERENDS

Dutch ethologist. Professor at the University of Groningen. He is one of the pioneers of the objectivist school and has published very many works dealing with highly varied animals. Among them, he has studied the return to the nest of the ammophila wasp, the behavior of guppies, and that of various seagulls.

NICOLAAS TINBERGEN

Dutch ethologist. Professor at Oxford University. Specialist in the stickleback and the silver seagull, he can be considered one of the founders of objectivism. The appearance of his work, *The Study of Instinct,* in 1951, rendered great service to animal psychology by triggering many discussions and establishing a universally accepted vocabulary.

P. P. GRASSE

Professor at the Sorbonne. Specialist in the ethology of termites and in those insects' building proclivities. He created a very lively French school devoted to the study of the social instincts of insects. He is director of publication of a very important *Treatise of Zoology*, in 17 volumes, constituting an incomparable reference work.

REMY CHAUVIN

French ethologist. Since presenting his doctoral thesis in 1942, he has published a very large number of works on ethology and especially social insects. His works have dealt with the effects of the group on the individuals, construction among ants, and the study of various substances playing a part in the social life of the hive. He has published several excellent works for the layman.

A Pertinent Glossary

A Pertinent Glossary

ANIMAL PSYCHOLOGY—Study of the psychic action (or psychism) of animals.

APPETITIVE BEHAVIOR—Phase preparatory to instinctive behavior; this phase, as opposed to instinct itself, is variable, not stereotyped.

APPRENTICESHIP—Term adopted by the author to denote the overall acquisition of knowledge by animals. This may take place within the natural conditions of wild life, or under planned experiment, and includes all acquisition of knowledge, whether through instinct, insight, intelligence, or reflex conditioning.

BIOLOGICAL BALANCE—Stable relationship of forces between different animal and vegetable species living within one given area and in more or less definite dependence upon each other; the blackbird, the gazelle, and the lion are three elements of a biological balance: any change made in one of the three elements will be reflected in the other two.

DECOY—Artifact duplicating a natural object, used by the experimenter to trigger a certain reaction in the animal. By varying the elements of the decoy, it is possible to isolate the significant stimulus or stimuli.

ECOLOGY—Study of the habitats of living beings.

ETHOLOGY—Study of the various behavior patterns of living beings.

HOME RANGE—See "Territory."

HYPERTELY—Excessive development of one morphological characteristic in the evolutionary development of a species.

IMPREGNATION—Form of quick and very stable apprenticeship which takes place at the start of life in social species. At this juncture, the zoopsychologist can study the great supra-individual characteristics of the species.

INSIGHT—Form of apprenticeship characterized by the sudden and permanent grasping of the correct solution.

MORPHOLOGY—Study of animal shapes. Those shapes themselves.

MOTIVATION—Complex of stimuli and external as well as internal states which lead to a given mode of behavior.

PSYCHISM (or: Psychic Action)—Collectivity of the phenomena of a higher order (intelligence, memory, instinct, etc.), usually in relation to the activity of the nervous system.

SIGNIFICANT STIMULUS—A stimulus which will have a definite effect upon a given animal at a given time of his life.

SOCIAL REACTOR—Characteristic of an animal to which any other animal of the same species will react.

STIMULUS—A change in the environment which triggers a change in some aspect of the animal's behavior.

TERRITORY (or: Home Range)—The zone defended by its occupant against competitors of his own species.

TROPHALLAXIS—Exchange of food between members of one social species.

VITAL DOMAIN—Area habitually frequented by an individual, a family, or a social group.

A Selected Bibliography

A Selected Bibliography

THIS bibliography, drawn up by the translator, includes the works referred to by the author and listed by him in the original, identified by an asterisk (*), as well as a selection of books currently available, mainly in English, in which the interested reader may find additional material related to the subjects treated in *Non-Human Thought*. Insofar as possible, name of publisher and date are given, in each case, for what appears to be the most readily accessible edition or editions.

ALLEE, W. C., *The Social Life of Animals* (Norton, New York 1938; Beacon paperback, 1958).

ALLEN, GLOVER. *Bats* (Harvard University Press, Cambridge, 1939; Dover paperback, 1962).

ALPERS, ANTHONY. *A Book of Dolphins* (John Murray, London, 1960).

———. *Dolphins: The Myth and the Mammal* (Houghton, Mifflin, Boston, 1961).

ARDREY, ROBERT. *African Genesis* (Atheneum, New York, 1961).

———. *The Territorial Imperative* (Atheneum, New York, 1966).

ARMSTRONG, E. A. *Bird Display and Behavior** (Dover, New York, 1964).

BOURLIER, FRANCOIS. *Vie et moeurs des mammifères** (Payot, Paris, 1951).

BROADHURST, P. L. *The Science of Animal Behavior* (Pelican, Baltimore, 1963).

CARTHY, J. D. *Animal Navigation: How Animals Find Their Way About* (Scribners, New York, 1956).

CHAUVIN, REMY. *Vie et moeurs des insectes** (Payot, Paris, 1956).

———. *Animal World** (Doubleday, Garden City, 1964).

CHEESMAN, EVELYN. *Insects: Their Secret World* (Apollo, New York, 1961).

CLARK, W. E. LEGROS. *History of the Primates* (University of Chicago Press, Chicago, 1957).

DARWIN, CHARLES R. *The Descent of Man** (Modern Library, Random House, New York).

――――. *The Expression of the Emotions in Man and Animals** (University of Chicago Press, Chicago, 1965).

DETHIER, V. G., and STELLAR, ELIOT. *Animal Behavior: Its Evolutionary and Neurological Basis* (Prentice-Hall, Englewood Cliffs, 1961).

DEVOE, ALAN. *This Fascinating Animal World* (McGraw-Hill, New York, 1951).

DOWDESWELL, W. H. *Animal Ecology* (Harper Torchbooks, New York, 1961).

FABRE, J. H. *Souvenirs entomologiques,** 10 vols. 1879-1907 (Delagrave, Paris, 1914-24). (Numerous partial English translations; also, see below: TEALE, EDWIN WAY.)

FRAENKEL, GOTTFRIED S., and GUNN, DONALD L. *The Orientation of Animals* (Clarendon Press, Oxford, 1940; Dover paperback, New York, 1961).

FRISCH, KARL VON. *Vie et moeurs des abeilles** (Albin Michel, Paris, 1955).

――――. *Bees: Their Vision, Chemical Senses and Language* (Cornell University Press, Ithaca, 1950; Great Seal paperback, New York, 1956).

――――. *The Dancing Bees* (Harcourt, Brace & World, New York, 1961).

GOETSCH, WILLIAM. *The Ants* (University of Michigan Press, Ann Arbor, 1957).

GRASSE, P. P. *Zoölogie** (Gallimard, Paris, 1963).

HEDIGER, HEINI. *Wild Animals in Captivity** (Dover, New York, 1950).

――――. *Studies of the Psychology and Behaviour of Captive Animals in Zoos and Circuses** (Butterworths Scientific Publications, London, 1955).

――――. *Observations sur la psychologie animale dans les parcs nationaux du Congo belge** (1951).

HEINROTH, OSKAR and KATHARINA. *The Birds* (University of Michigan Press, Ann Arbor, 1958).

JACOBS, JAKE. *Marineland Diver* (Dodd, Mead, New York, 1960).

JENNINGS, H. S. *Behavior of the Lower Organisms** (Indiana University Press, Bloomington, 1962).

――――. *Genetics of Protozoa* (Nijhoff, The Hague, 1929).

KELLOGG, W. N. *Porpoises and Sonar** (University of Chicago Press, Chicago, 1961).

KOHLER, WOLFGANG. *The Mentality of Apes** (Humanities Press, New York, 1956).

KULLENBERG, BERTIL. *Studies in Ophrys Pollination** (Almqvist & Wiksells, Uppsala, 1961).

LANYON, W. E., and TAVOLGA, W. N. *Animal Sounds and Communication* (American Institute of Biological Studies, Washington, Publication No. 7, 1960).

LECOMTE, JACQUES. *Les animaux** (Flammarion, Paris, 1962).

LILLY, JOHN C. *Man and Dolphin** (Doubleday, Garden City, 1961; Pyramid paperback, 1962).

LOEB, JACQUES. *Forced Movements, Tropisms and Animal Conduct** (Lippincott, Philadelphia & London, 1918).

LORENZ, KONRAD, *Les animaux inconnus** (Editions de Paris, Paris, 1953).

———. *King Solomon's Ring** (Methuen, London, 1952).

———. *Man Meets Dog** (Methuen, London, 1954).

———. *On Aggression* (Harcourt, Brace & World, New York, 1966).

LUBBOCK, SIR JOHN. *Ants, Bees and Wasps** (Appleton, New York, 1882).

MAETERLINCK, MAURICE. *The Life of the Bee** (Dodd, Mead, New York, 1901; Mentor paperback, New York, 1954).

———. *The Life of the Ant** (John Day, New York, 1930).

MATTHEWS, G. V. T. *Bird Navigation** (Cambridge University Press, Cambridge, 1955).

MORLEY, DEREK W. *The Ant World* (Pelican, Baltimore, 1953).

———. *Ants* (Collins, London, 1953).

MORRIS, DESMOND. *The Biology of Art** (Knopf, New York, 1962).

NORMAN, J. R., and FRASER, F. C. *Field Book of Giant Fishes, Whales, and Dolphins* (Putnam, London, 1937).

PAVLOV, I. P. *Conditioned Reflexes** (Oxford University Press, London, 1927; Dover paperback, New York, 1960).

———. *Conditioned Reflexes and Psychiatry** (International Publishers, New York, 1963).

RICHARDS, O. W. *Social Insects* (Philosophical Library, New York, 1953; Harper Torchbooks, New York, 1961).

SCHILLER, CLAIRE H. (translator-editor). *Instinctive Behavior** (International Universities Press, New York, 1957).

SCOTT, JOHN PAUL. *Animal Behavior* (University of Chicago Press, Chicago, 1958; Anchor paperback, Garden City, 1963).

SKAIFE, S. H. *Dwellers in Darkness* (Longmans, Green, New York & London, 1955; Anchor paperback, Garden City, 1961).

SPITZ, RENE. *No and Yes* (International Universities Press, New York, 1957).

STUART, FRANK S. *City of the Bees* (McGraw-Hill, New York, 1949).

TEALE, EDWIN WAY. *A Book about Bees* (Midland paperback, Bloomington, 1959).

———. *The Fascinating Insect World of J. Henri Fabre* (Premier paperback, New York, 1956).

———. *The Insect World of J. Henri Fabre* (Apollo paperback, New York, 1961).

THORPE, W. H., and ZANGWILL, O. L. *Current Problems in Animal Behaviour** (Cambridge University Press, Cambridge, 1961).

TINBERGEN, NIKO (NICOLAAS). *The Study of Instinct** (Clarendon Press, Oxford, 1951).

———. *Carnets d'un naturaliste** (Hachette, Paris, 1951).

———. *Curious Naturalists* (Basic Books, New York, 1959).

WALLACE, BRUCE, and SRB, ADRIAN M. *Adaptation* (2nd ed., Prentice-Hall, Englewood Cliffs, 1964).

YERKES, R. M. *The Great Apes** (Yale University Press, New Haven, 1929).

———. *Chimpanzees: A Laboratory Colony** (Yale University Press, New Haven, 1943).

RELEVANT PERIODICALS

American Journal of Psychiatry, Washington, D.C.
Animal Behaviour,* London
Behaviour,* Leiden, Netherlands
Biological Bulletin, Woods Hole, Mass.
Bulletin of Marine Science of the Gulf & Caribbean, Miami, Fla.
Hvalraadets Skrifter, Academy of Sciences, Oslo, Norway
Insectes sociaux,* Paris
Journal of the Acoustical Society of America, New York City
Journal of Applied Physiology, Washington, D.C.
Journal of Comparitive & Physiological Psychology,* Washington, D.C.
Journal of Experimental Zoology, Philadelphia
Journal of Mammalogy, Lawrence, Kan.
Science, Washington, D.C.
Scientific American, New York City
Zeitschrift für Tierphysiologie,* Hamburg, Germany
Zoologica, Bronx, New York

Index

Index